THE CYCLING PUZZLE BOOK

NEIL SOMERVILLE

summersdale

An Hachette UK Company
www.hachette.co.uk

Summersdale Publishers Ltd
Part of Octopus Publishing Group Limited
Carmelite House
50 Victoria Embankment
LONDON
EC4Y 0DZ
UK

www.summersdale.com

Printed and bound in Poland

ISBN: 978-1-80007-004-2

*This book is dedicated to you and everyone
in the cycling community.*

Thank you.

INTRODUCTION

Cycling is one of life's great pleasures. Most of us learned to cycle when young and over the years this will have opened up many opportunities. Whether you choose to race, perform tricks, explore new areas, keep fit or just gain a bit more freedom, cycling offers so much.

And it is fun.

This book is a celebration of cycling, but in another way. Rather than exercising the body, here is a chance to let cycling exercise the brain. There are all sorts of puzzles to enjoy, including mystery sudokus, word searches and criss-crosses. Plus, you can figure out what famous cyclists have said as well as deliberate over the meaning of cycling terms such as "bonk" and "squirrel".

Cycling in its many forms brings a great deal of joy. And no matter whether you're an occasional cyclist or someone who takes it more seriously, I hope *The Cycling Puzzle Book* will entertain, surprise and hold many delights.

Enjoy the ride.

Neil Somerville

ANAGRAMS

Unscramble the following to reveal some parts of a bike.

1. TOP ASSET

2. NUT IN BEER

3. LAPSED

4. A RASH BLEND

5. AH! DELIGHT

TAKE YOUR PICK

Which of the following is the correct answer? Take your pick.

1. In 1868, a British manufacturing company received an order from France to make some Velocipedes, an early type of bicycle. What did this company usually make?
    a) Gun carriages
    b) Sewing machines
    c) Locks

2. Georges Passerieu won the Paris–Roubaix race in 1907, but during the race he was stopped by a gendarme. Why?
    a) The gendarme thought Passerieu was cycling too fast and was a danger to pedestrians.
    b) In view of the colourful clothes that Passerieu was wearing, the gendarme thought the cyclist was from a touring circus and was trying to get in on the action.
    c) The gendarme wanted to check that Passerieu had the correct tax plate on his bike.

3. The fictional detective Sherlock Holmes was once called to investigate *The Adventure of...*
    a) *the Long Distance Cyclist*
    b) *the Disappearing Cyclist*
    c) *the Solitary Cyclist*

MYSTERY SUDOKU

Complete the grid so that every row, column and 3 × 3 box contains the letters ACEHILMOS in any order. One row or column contains a seven-letter word that is something many cyclists use. What is it?

	E				H			
	L			E				M
				O	I		L	
		S			M	O		
O		E				H		S
		H	S			C		
	I		O	L				
A				M			S	
			H				O	

CYCLING WORDS

What do the following words mean?

1. BONK
a) To fall off
b) A state of severe exhaustion
c) To hit a pothole

2. BIDON
a) Water bottle
b) Knee strap
c) Brake cable

3. CAPTAIN
a) Race umpire (whose decision is final!)
b) Defending champion
c) First person on a tandem

4. FARTLEK
a) A handicap race with cyclists grouped according to ability
b) A vintage bicycle race (usually for bicycles manufactured before 1960)
c) A training technique based on varying pace and intensity

CROSS OUT

Cross out all the letters that appear more than once. The letters that are left, reading from top to bottom and left to right, will spell out something well known. What is it?

D	H	P	W	T	L	F	S
Z	K	Q	E	O	G	A	R
N	V	J	Y	S	U	V	C
P	G	W	N	C	B	K	A
L	Z	D	O	M	E	Y	U
Q	H	X	T	J	R	F	V

CRYPTOGRAM

Cyclist, engineer and author Jobst Brandt wrote much about the value of cycling and the bicycle. Solve the cryptogram to discover some of his thoughts. To give you a start, R = S, A = Y and G = L.

```
┌─┬─┬─┬─┬─┬─┬─┬─┬─┬─┬─┬─┐
│T│V│█│F│R│V│█│H│W│█│O│M│Q│
├─┼─┼─┼─┼─┼─┼─┼─┼─┼─┼─┼─┤
│ │ │█│ │S│ │█│ │ │█│ │ │ │
└─┴─┴─┴─┴─┴─┴─┴─┴─┴─┴─┴─┘
```

```
┌─┬─┬─┬─┬─┬─┬─┬─┬─┬─┬─┬─┬─┬──┬─┬─┬─┬─┬─┬──┐
│W│Q│I│D│R│N│M│Q│W│I│W│H│M│D,│█│R│N│M│Q│W,│
├─┼─┼─┼─┼─┼─┼─┼─┼─┼─┼─┼─┼─┼──┼─┼─┼─┼─┼─┼──┤
│ │ │ │ │S│ │ │ │ │ │ │ │ │ ,│█│ │S│ │ │ ,│
└─┴─┴─┴─┴─┴─┴─┴─┴─┴─┴─┴─┴─┴──┴─┴─┴─┴─┴─┴──┘
```

```
┌─┬─┬─┬─┬─┬─┬─┬─┬──┬─┬─┬─┬─┬─┬─┐
│Q│V│K│Q│V│I│W│H│M D,│█│I│D│E│█│S│I│L│V│
├─┼─┼─┼─┼─┼─┼─┼─┼──┼─┼─┼─┼─┼─┼─┤
│ │ │ │ │ │ │ │ │  ,│█│ │ │ │█│ │ │ │ │
└─┴─┴─┴─┴─┴─┴─┴─┴──┴─┴─┴─┴─┴─┴─┘
```

```
┌─┬─┬─┬─┬─┬─┬─┬─┬─┬─┐
│H│W│█│I│█│T│I│A│█│M│O│█│G│H│O│V│
├─┼─┼─┼─┼─┼─┼─┼─┼─┼─┤
│ │ │█│ │█│ │ │Y│█│ │ │█│L│ │ │ │
└─┴─┴─┴─┴─┴─┴─┴─┴─┴─┘
```

WORD SEARCH: BIKE PARTS

Find the following bike parts hidden in the wheel.

Bearing	Pannier
Brake	Pedal
Cable	Reflector
Cassette	Saddle
Chain	Spindle
Derailleur	Spoke
Fork	Sprocket
Frame	Tyre
Handlebar	Valve
Inner tube	Wheel

A RIDDLE

My first is in racing but not in sprint,
My second is in help but not in hint.
My third is in race but never in speed,
My fourth is in repair but not in need.
My fifth is in first as well as in last,
And my whole can help you go fast.

What am I?

9

SPOT THE DIFFERENCE

Can you spot seven differences between the two pictures?

CROSSWORD

Solve the clues and discover in the shaded squares what can be a short but challenging race. Not one for the faint-hearted! What is it?

Across

1 Tyre problem (8)

5 Stopping mechanism (6)

9 Make easier (8)

10 Brief look (6)

11 Overshadowed (8)

12 Prohibited (6)

14 Training wheels (10)

18 Agreeing (10)

22 Track cycling event (6)

23 Charitable gift (8)

24 Trying experience (6)

25 Flying (8)

26 Rider's seat (6)

27 So gained (anagram) (8)

Down

1 Overtook (6)

2 Agile (6)

3 Spring flowers (6)

4 Found on mudguards (10)

6 Dependable (8)

7 Good deed (8)

8 Buyers (8)

13 Leaving (10)

15 Cutting instrument (8)

16 Trespassed (8)

17 Run away (4, 4)

19 Bike frame material (6)

20 Wispy cloud (6)

21 Mean to (6)

MINI SUDOKU: WARM-UP

Before any race or lengthy cycle, it is important to warm up and prepare yourself physically. In this mini sudoku, complete the grid so that every row, column and 2 × 3 box contains the letters that make up "warm-up". As this is the first mini sudoku in the book, hopefully this will be a warm-up for the others that appear later.

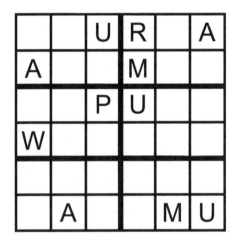

STRANGE BUT TRUE

What unusual occurrence took place in Wisbech, Cambridgeshire, on 21 April 1897?

a) The newly formed Wisbech Town Football Club needed to raise funds to buy a more permanent pitch. To help raise money, the players held a sponsored bike race around the town. It was so successful the players turned this into an annual event, which continued until the outbreak of the First World War.

b) A cycle wedding took place. The bride and bridesmaids rode to the church on "safety bicycles" and the bridegroom and best man rode together on a "sociable bicycle". After the service the newlyweds used the sociable bicycle to cycle round the town with many guests following behind, also on bikes.

c) A robbery took place at a jewellery shop in the centre of Wisbech. Arriving at the scene just minutes after the crime, a policeman borrowed a bicycle and successfully chased and caught the robber. The chief constable was so impressed he ensured every police station in the area was provided with a bicycle.

WORD LADDER

Whether it's for securing or transporting your wheels, a bike rack certainly has its uses. In this word ladder, change one letter at a time to turn – or transport – the word "bike" into "rack".

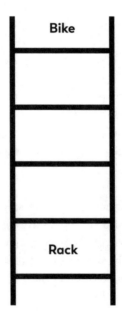

LETTER DROP

The letters in each of the columns need to be entered into the squares immediately below, but not necessarily in the same order. By placing the letters in the correct places you will reveal an observation from long-distance cyclist Heinz Stücke which will also ring true with many.

	O		K	E		W			
	T	U	N	N		T	Y		
	O	W	N	I	S		T	H	
		I	R	N	N	D		M	H	E
	C	R	U	H	E	R	O	S	H	A
	A	T	U	R	E	S	L	T	N	E	T

STAR NAME

The letters of the name of a well-known British cyclist have been spread evenly around the circle. Find the first letter in the cyclist's name and follow the letters in order, thereby completing the star – and the star's name. Who is the cyclist?

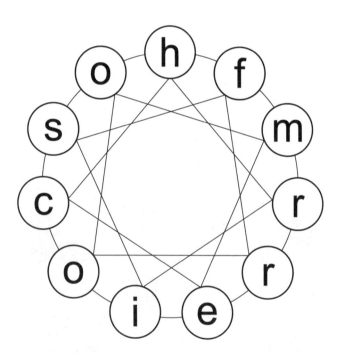

WORD QUEST: BICYCLE

The humble bicycle is supremely versatile, whether you use it for transport, sport or just to ride for fun. Here is a chance to consider the bicycle in another way. Make as many words of three or more letters out of "bicycle" as you can. No names.

BICYCLE

10 words = excellent
8 words = very good
6 words = good

CODED CROSSWORD

Each letter of the alphabet has been replaced by a number. To solve the puzzle, you must decide which letter is represented by which number. To help you start, one of the words has been partly filled in. When you have solved the code, complete the bottom grid to discover something challenging for mountain bikers. What is it?

1	2	3	4	5	6	7	8	9	10 C	11	12	13 A
14	15	16	17	18	19	20	21 B	22	23	24	25	26

6	20	10	22		5	13	6	18	25	1

FITTING WORDS

Fit the following words into the grid so that another word is created in the shaded squares – it's something that is an important consideration for cyclists.

CHASE
CLASSIC
FANFARE
OUTFIT
PRIZES
RAPID
TOOLBOX

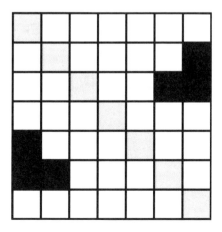

BIKE JUMBLE

Various parts of a bike have been discarded and jumbled up below. Join the bits together to reassemble eight bike components.

DL   FR   MU   LEC   DA

LS   EB   SAD   ARS

RES   PE   TY   REF   AME

AKES   HAN   DLE   ARD

DGU   BR   TOR

MYSTERY SUDOKU

Complete the grid so that every row, column and 3 × 3 box contains the letters AEFGHIRST in any order. One row or column contains something (two words) found on many bikes. What is it?

	R		E		F	T	H	
				R				E
			G		F			
I				T		E		
		F				A		
		A		S				T
		H		A				
R			T					
	F	E	H		G		I	

WHAT THEY SAID

The following quotes have some of their words missing. What did the following write or say?

1. Geraint Thomas has many achievements to his name, including winning the 2018 Tour de France. In considering what gets a rider to the top, what were his thoughts?

   "Determination, for sure, and some raw talent, and great coaching, and..."
   a) a good bike.
   b) a little luck.
   c) discipline.

2. John Tomac, when considering the Mammoth Mountain's Kamikaze downhill race, said:

   "You don't get scared. ..."
   a) It wastes energy.
   b) You just prepare.
   c) You don't have time to be.

3. What did Olympic gold medallist champion Laura Kenny (née Trott) write?

   "The minute I sit on the bike, ..."
   a) I am like a different person.
   b) there's no holding me back. I'm off and away.
   c) I get pedalling. It's what I do.

WORD BUILDER

The letters of part of a bike have been numbered 1 to 9. Solve the clues to discover what it is. The answer is two words.

Letters 3, 1 and 8 give us a pen point

Letters 2, 7 and 6 give us a hard fruit

Letters 6, 4, 5 and 2 give us a seabird

Letters 6, 5, 7 and 9 give us something genuine

Letters 8, 4, 9 and 5 give us something to drink. Cheers!

1	2	3	4	5	6	7	8	9

FIND THE BIKE

There is just one bicycle hidden in the grid below. It could be written across, down or diagonally, either forwards or backwards, but it is in a straight line. Can you find the bicycle?

```
E  L  I  B  I  C  B  I  I  C  B  I  C  B  E
B  C  L  C  E  Y  L  Y  E  L  I  E  L  Y  E
Y  E  C  Y  B  E  C  B  C  C  I  C  I  C  C
E  B  I  C  I  C  Y  L  Y  B  B  E  L  L  B
I  B  L  Y  C  E  C  I  C  L  E  I  C  L  C
C  B  E  L  Y  I  L  C  Y  B  C  L  Y  B  E
L  I  E  B  L  B  B  C  I  B  L  E  B  Y  I
B  Y  L  E  I  E  I  L  Y  C  B  L  L  C  E
Y  B  C  E  L  C  I  C  C  L  B  I  Y  B  C
C  B  I  E  I  B  E  E  L  E  C  L  C  I  E
Y  C  I  C  L  C  I  Y  I  C  E  B  C  Y  I
B  E  L  L  Y  B  Y  E  C  B  Y  I  L  C  B
C  I  B  B  Y  C  C  B  Y  L  I  C  Y  L  E
I  L  C  I  E  Y  L  C  I  C  E  L  C  I  C
B  E  B  C  L  I  C  E  L  C  B  I  C  L  B
```

A PERPLEXING POSER

The letters of a certain day of the week can be reordered to spell something found on some bikes. What is the day and what can it be changed to?

MAZE

Time for a cycle – but as it's in the circle, you can take a roundabout route. Find your way to the centre.

MISSING PART

Insert the name of a bike part so that, reading down, five five-letter words are formed. What is the bike part?

C	C	D	A	A
A	H	E	T	R
T	S	I	A	N
I	E	T	S	A

CRISS-CROSS: BMX TRICKS

There are lots of BMX tricks to master and have fun with. Show some *flair* and *drop* all the following into the grid. To do *nothing* is, dare I say, a bit *feeble*. Good luck.

4-letter trick
Drop

5-letter tricks
Fakie
Flair

6-letter tricks
Decade
Feeble
Invert
Nac-Nac
No Foot
Nollie

7-letter tricks
Barspin
Crooked
Full Cab

Grizzly
Icepick
Nothing
Tri Star

8-letter tricks
Alleyoop
Bunny Hop
Lookback
Tabletop
Toboggan
Turndown
Wallride

9-letter tricks
Crankflip
Crossfoot
Frontflip
Nose Pivot

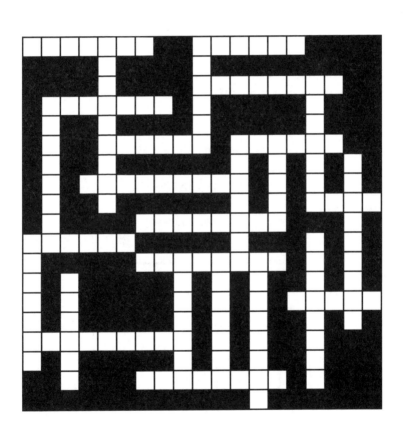

PRIZED SURPRISE

Solve the following clues and in two of the down columns you will discover something that is much prized by some cyclists. What is the prized surprise?

1. Nightwear

2. Customer response

3. Dancing venue

4. Foot levers

5. Brave people

6. Ostentatious

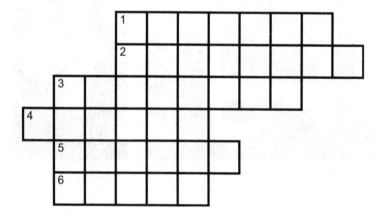

STRANGE BUT TRUE

Why was the Havant Grand Prix, an international cycling race which had been running for 16 years in the UK, called off in 2006?

a) There were fears that the new route would pass too close to a golf course and put the cyclists in danger of being struck by golf balls.

b) It was stopped on safety grounds as the organizers of the race were unable to address the issue of cyclists relieving themselves on the side of the road.

c) Given the large numbers of spectators and visitors arriving to watch the race, there was great concern that road verges, gardens, parks and flower borders would get trampled over.

CRYPTOGRAM

Solve the cryptogram to reveal an observation from Daniel Behrman, author of *The Man Who Loved Bicycles*. To give you a start, P = D and E = S.

G	T	N		R	U	O	W	P		W	M	N	E		O	M	F	T	G
								D					S						

Q	N	L	U	C	P		G	T	N		T	I	C	P	W	N	Q	I	O	E
					D								D							S

U	D		I	C	L		Q	M	Z	L	Z	W	N

A PICTURE POSER

What is suggested by the following? Something not to be ignored when it comes to your bike.

DOUBLE TAKE

The names of some bike parts have two different meanings: one for a bike part and another for something else. So, for example, the answer to the clue "lightning stroke (4)" would be "bolt". Solve the clues below and name the bike parts. The number of letters in the answer is given in brackets.

1. Junction (4)

2. Link (5)

3. Relevance (7)

4. Burden (6)

5. Hard-shelled seed (3)

6. Equipment (4)

MINI SUDOKU: SPRINT

Perhaps you enjoy a sprint on your own bike or watching an exciting sprint finish in competitive cycling. Well, here's a chance to enjoy a sprint in another way. In this mini sudoku, complete the grid so that every row, column and 2 × 3 box contains the letters that make up the word "sprint".

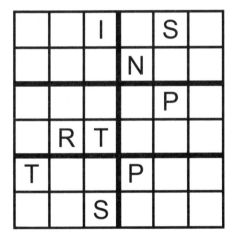

TAKE YOUR PICK

Which of the following is the correct answer? Take your pick.

1. Where did the phrase "bicycle built for two" come from?
   a) It was the title of a Laurel and Hardy film. They needed to get to the film studios quickly, with a bicycle as the only means of transport. They set about modifying the bike so they could both ride it.
   b) It was used to advertise the first manufactured tandems in the late nineteenth century.
   c) It was from the lyrics of a song.

2. In 2009 students at Massachusetts Institute of Technology invented the Bicilavadora, but what was this designed to do?
   a) Wash clothes. It was a drum fitted on a frame and powered by a bicycle chain.
   b) It was a bicycle which could be adapted to fit on to, and operate, a pedalo.
   c) It was a robotic bicycle programmed to ride between university buildings carrying books and other small portable items.

3. The Giro di Lombardia, officially Il Lombardia, is a cycling race in Lombardy, Italy. It was first held in 1905 and is the final "monument" of the cycling season. What is this race known as? The Race of...
   a) Hills
   b) Vineyards
   c) the Falling Leaves

STAR NAME

The letters of the name of a well-known British cyclist have been spread evenly around the circle. Find the first letter in the cyclist's name and follow the letters, thereby completing the star – and the star's name. Who is the cyclist?

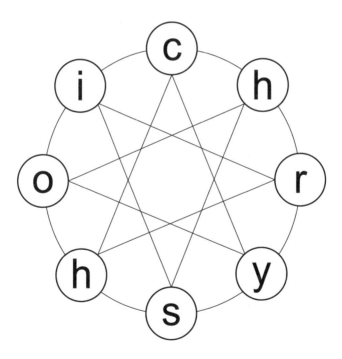

WORD SEARCH: TOUR DE FRANCE WINNERS

In this word search, seek out the following winners of one of the world's most popular sporting events, the Tour de France.

Anquetil
Bernal
Bobet
Contador
Evans
Fignon
Frantz
Froome
Hinault
Induráin
Leducq

LeMond
Maes
Merckx
Nibali
Pogacar
Riis
Sastre
Thomas
Thys
Ullrich
Wiggins

```
O L C I B L D I S X M O W B V W R
A U D P A K A Q N K V X P D R I R
R Q J N O E W V O C C B Q O J G Z
W V R W K G E L K R F H D T E G D
C E D T R P A N E E Y A S M F I W
B W U X L E I C M M T F O R K N C
E X P N S A F E A N O O A M R S W
I N P G R A K S O R R N B W F L X
M K G U R N S C I F T T D Q O Y P
W J D P O Q L T A Z E V A N S T P
E N F N U E B I R O L V A D T L V
I N G B Q L O S T E E J B W S U A
A I C V B V B E G E D O E B A A H
F B D J R T E A J B U S Q S M N S
F A Q Y H C T M D S C Q S E O I D
W L E Y S I I R B S Q C N X H H S
F I S N H W U L L R I C H A T E W
```

CYCLING WORDS

What do the following words mean?

1. ORTHOTICS
a) Custom-made supports worn in cycling shoes
b) Rash caused by chafing
c) Muscle cramp

2. DOSSARD
a) Member of support team
b) Bunch of cyclists trailing the leaders
c) Number worn on the back of a cyclist's jersey

3. SALMON
a) To cycle down a one-way street in the wrong direction
b) To skid
c) A pile-up or crash involving quite a few cyclists

4. BRICK
a) To fall off
b) A rider who is a slow climber but an efficient descender
c) To have a run of bad form and disappointing results

LETTER DROP

The letters in each of the columns need to be entered into the squares immediately below, but not necessarily in the same order. By placing the letters in the correct places you will reveal an observation from actor and comedian Robin Williams.

WORD LADDER

Weather can make a big difference in cycling, especially if you have a tailwind to assist your efforts. In this word ladder, change one letter at a time to turn "tail" into "wind". Hopefully this will be a breeze.

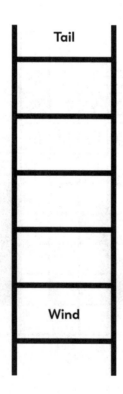

Tail

Wind

ON TRACK

Find the start. Then, moving one letter at a time – either horizontally, vertically or diagonally – discover something that cyclists should not ignore. What is it? The answer is two words.

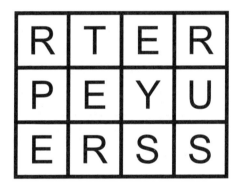

R	T	E	R
P	E	Y	U
E	R	S	S

DOWN WORD

Place a three-letter word in the spaces in each row to complete a six-letter word. When the grid is completed correctly, a new word in the shaded squares will be formed. This is something essential for cyclists. What is it?

			O	R	Y
			M	I	T
			O	W	S
			A	C	T
			T	A	L
			L	U	S

WHAT HAPPENED NEXT?

What happened to Finnish opera star Esa Ruuttunen when he cycled to a rehearsal at the Helsinki Opera House in 2006?

1. A squirrel ran into his bicycle, causing the singer to fall off. He was knocked out and broke his nose.

2. To help promote the forthcoming production, he rode to the final rehearsal in costume. Unfortunately, some of the costume tangled in the wheels and the singer and bike fell over. An ambulance had to be called and, with the singer still attached to his bike, he was taken to a nearby hospital. Ruuttunen quickly recovered. The bike did not.

3. A manuscript the singer had been working on blew out of his pannier. Seeing what had happened, two traffic policemen stopped the traffic so the singer and some helpful passers-by could gather up the loose pages. In gratitude the singer gave the policemen, and those who assisted, tickets for the opening night.

MYSTERY SUDOKU

Complete the grid so that every row, column and 3 × 3 box contains the letters ABCILNRTU in any order. One row or column contains a nine-letter word which is something essential for bike maintenance. What is it?

	L	C		B			I	
		I			R	N	L	
					T			
				I		A	N	
			B		A			
	C	N		T				
			C					
	B	R	N				I	
		I			A		C	U

A RIDDLE

My first is in stop but not in go,
My second is in speed, never in slow.
My third is in road but not in race,
My fourth is in quick, never in pace.
My fifth is in embark but not in start,
And my whole is a vital bike part.

What am I?

CODED CROSSWORD

Each letter of the alphabet has been replaced by a number. To solve the puzzle, you must decide which letter is represented by which number. To help you start, one of the words has been partly filled in. When you have solved the code, complete the bottom grid to discover what can be an exciting feature of many a race or stage.

ANAGRAM CHALLENGE

The following anagrams all have a connection and collectively they make

ROADS GRUNT

Unscramble them and work out the connection.

1. NOT CURED FEAR

2. O! A RIGID TAIL

3. EVALUATES A NAP

NATIONAL CHAMPIONS

Over the years, many cyclists have made their home nations proud. Here's a chance to acknowledge some of the greats and match them with their country.

1. Marianne Vos   a) America

2. Bernard Hinault   b) Ireland

3. Alison Sydor   c) Spain

4. Eddy Merckx   d) Australia

5. Stephen Roche   e) Netherlands

6. Greg LeMond   f) Italy

7. Peter Sagan   g) France

8. Miguel Induráin   h) Canada

9. Cadel Evans   i) Belgium

10. Fausto Coppi   j) Slovakia

CROSS OUT

Cross out all the letters that appear more than once. The letters that are left, reading from top to bottom and left to right, will spell out something essential for the bicycle. What is it?

M	C	P	V	R	G	H	D
K	Q	W	J	F	S	X	U
V	E	N	Y	M	H	K	T
F	Z	D	P	H	X	C	G
J	M	S	U	O	Z	Q	Y
N	I	W	E	T	L	G	R

CRISS-CROSS: GIRO D'ITALIA WINNERS

All the following have triumphed in the Giro d'Italia but can you triumph by finding the right place for each of these winners in the grid?

4-letter name
Gaul

5-letter names
Basso
Binda
Coppi
Gotti
Magni
Roche

6-letter names
Bernal
Fignon
Froome
Merckx
Nibali
Simoni

7-letter names
Baldini

Bartali
Carapaz
Gimondi
Hinault
Pantani
Saronni
Valetti

8-letter names
Anquetil
Contador
Dumoulin
Hesjedal
Induráin

9-letter name
Balmamion

13-letter name
Geoghegan Hart

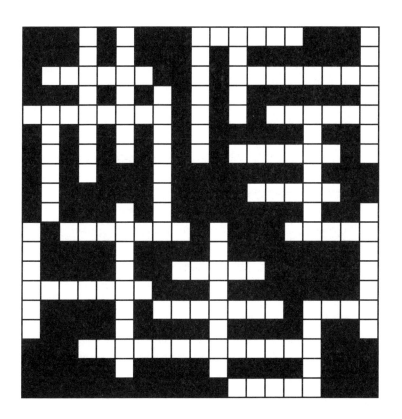

STRANGE BUT TRUE

Hugo Koblet was a successful Swiss cyclist who won the Giro d'Italia in 1950, the Tour de France in 1951 and many other major races. Koblet quickly appreciated the power of the media in professional cycling. What did he do that set him apart from others?

a) He hired a highly attractive PR manager, who not only drew attention to herself but in the process also ensured Koblet got plenty of coverage.

b) He took lessons in acting so that he could present himself well and also hired a scriptwriter so his interviews were full of one-liners and suitable soundbites. He was an interviewer's dream.

c) He kept a comb and sponge soaked in eau de cologne in his racing jersey. This allowed him to freshen up before the end of a race so he looked good in the photographs.

BETWEEN THE WHEELS

Something many cyclists enjoy and some specialize in can be inserted between the wheels so that, reading downward, eight three-letter words can be formed. What is this pleasure and exciting discipline?

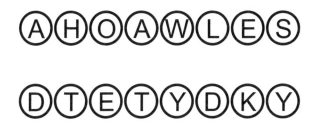

CRYPTOGRAM

Solve the cryptogram to discover an interesting observation. The name of the person who said this is also part of the puzzle. To give you a start, U = R and F = M.

E	P	W	D		P	I		E	P	L	D		U	P	A	P	S	C
													R					

R		K	P	Z	G	Z	E	D.		B	V		L	D	D	N
								.								

G	V	O	U		K	R	E	R	S	Z	D		G	V	O
			R												

F	O	I	B		L	D	D	N		F	V	H	P	S	C.
M										M					.

R	E	K	D	U	B		D	P	S	I	B	D	P	S
				R										

WORD LADDER

In order to keep our bikes safe, almost all of us have a bike lock. In this word ladder, change one letter at a time to turn "bike" into "lock".

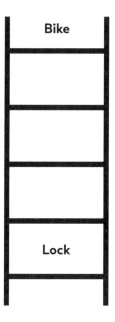

Bike

Lock

A PERPLEXING POSER

Sara was keen to support her husband and three of his friends as they practised for a forthcoming race. So she could get a good view of the cyclists and cheer them on, she stood on top of a bridge she knew they would be cycling under. She was there at just the right time, had an unimpeded view, there was nothing wrong with her vision, and it was daylight. The practice went ahead as planned. However, while she was there, Sara did not see a single cyclist. How come?

ACROSTICS

Solve the clues correctly and the shaded squares will reveal something important and necessary. What is it?

1. Appearance, view
2. Captured
3. Counterbalance
4. Flaw
5. Hit
6. Road around a town

1					
2					
3					
4					
5					
6					

WORD SEARCH: WINNERS OF THE VUELTA A ESPAÑA

Find the following victors of this gruelling multi-stage race which is primarily held in Spain.

Altig
Anquetil
Aru
Bracke
Contador
Delgado
Deloor
Froome
Fuente
Gimondi
Heras
Hinault
Horner
Kelly

Menchov
Merckx
Nibali
Pingeon
Pino
Quintana
Rodriguez
Roglic
Rominger
Ruiz
Ullrich
Valverde
Yates
Zülle

```
Z A Z S Z Z S A R E H H E S K C Z
E M M N B A Q M H G C I V L O F I
U E F G V U E N O I E A N F L O U
G N F A E R X S R U M Y W A C U R
I C G B C X F L N J O L I D U L Z
R H C K B D L B E Y O L L E B L G
D O X E N U E L R Y R E A L N I T
O V A Z C Q X L E A F K B O M L T
R Q W L F C M J G Z C L I O X Z F
J A D R T C R G A A T K N R A O V
D R J Z X I N I V Q D D E N O A U
F U I P I N G E O N I O A N L R T
U R O D A T N O C R I T I V O N S
E G R O M I N G E R N P E G Z E P
N L I T E U Q N A I O R L N T P H
T Z T J Q S B Z U Z D I T A F L N
E I G A U W Q Q B E C T Y U L R Z
```

WHAT THEY SAID

The following are quotations but with some words missing. What did the following people write or say?

1. In writing about weather conditions, champion cyclist Geraint Thomas gave them human characteristics. *"Rain is cruel. Sun is all smiles but slowly stitches you up."* What did he think about the wind? *"Wind is..."*

   a) sly.
   b) petulant.
   c) mean.

2. Henri Desgrange, founder of the Tour de France, commented, *"The ideal Tour would be a Tour in which..."*

   a) there was a crazy sprint to the finish.
   b) only one rider survived the ordeal.
   c) only the best were left to fight it out.

3. Jacques Anquetil, French cyclist and five-time winner of the Tour de France, observed, *"There are no races. ..."*

   a) Only lotteries.
   b) Only battles with self and others.
   c) It's a business.

MINI SUDOKU: BRAKES

Time for a break of sorts. In this mini sudoku, complete the grid so that every row, column and 2 × 3 box contains the letters that make up the word "brakes".

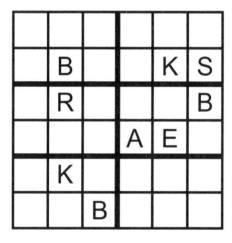

	B			K	S
	R				B
			A	E	
	K				
		B			

WORD BUILDER

The letters of something many cyclists value and appreciate have been numbered 1 to 9. Solve the clues to discover what it is. The answer is two words.

Letters 7, 8 and 2 give us whichever

Letters 3, 6, 7 and 2 give us some sticky earth

Letters 4, 7, 1 and 9 give us some delicate fabric

Letters 7, 6, 4, 9 and 2 give us a passageway

Letters 1, 7, 8, 3, 5 and 6 cause us to call off

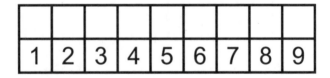

A PICTURE POSER

What is suggested by the following?

ANAGRAMS

"And Cycle" is an anagram of British cyclist Ed Clancy, but can you unscramble the following to reveal the names of some other well-known British cyclists?

1. A STORMING HEAT

2. MIND HAVERSACK

3. HEROIC FORMS

4. NANNY JOKES

5. DIG BY LARGE WINS

TRUE OR FALSE?

Decide whether the following statements are true or false.

1. BMX racing was included in the Olympics for the first time at the 2008 Games in Beijing, China.

2. One of the first safety bicycles was called the Kangaroo.

3. Eddy Merckx was 10 when he first learned to ride a bike. Up until then he had no interest in cycling, much preferring running and football instead.

4. The former French president Charles de Gaulle was a keen cyclist and, in his youth, entered the Tour de France.

5. The Wright brothers, who in 1903 achieved the first powered and controlled airplane flight, also had a shop where they made and sold bicycles.

6. Before turning to cycling, American star Greg LeMond had ambitions to become a professional swimmer.

CRISS-CROSS: BIKE PARTS

A bike has many components. Here's a chance to gather some of them together by fitting them all in the grid.

3-letter words
Cup
Hub
Rim

4-letter words
Axle
Cone
Fork
Rack
Stem
Tyre

5-letter words
Brake
Chain
Frame
Pedal
Spoke
Valve
Wheel

6-letter words
Cogset
Dynamo

Gusset
Saddle

7-letter words
Bar ends
Bearing
Coupler
Ferrule
Headset
Locknut
Shifter
Spindle

8-letter words
Cassette
Mudguard
Seat post

9-letter words
Handlebar
Inner tube

10-letter word
Derailleur

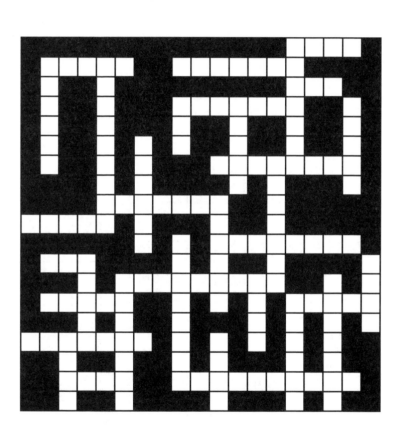

LETTER DROP

The letters in each of the columns need to be entered into the squares immediately below, but not necessarily in the same order. By placing the letters in the correct places you will reveal a thought from the 35th American president, John F. Kennedy, and one I am sure many will agree with.

	B		S	I		P		
A	N	A	S	R	I	S	D	
P	L	E	O	K	H	M	N	G	T	E
C	O	E	P	A	U	R	R	L	O	O
T	H	M	I	T	E	E	E	I	E	F

TAKE YOUR PICK

Which of the following is the correct answer? Take your pick.

1. Maurice Garin won the inaugural Tour de France in 1903, although the following year he was disqualified. Why?

   a) Garin got his supporters to alter signposts, thus sending competitors the wrong way.

   b) Rather than ride some of the longer stages, he caught a train instead.

   c) To maintain his lead, Garin arranged with a local farmer that once he had crossed a certain bridge the farmer would block it with a hay wagon. This meant the other competitors had to make a lengthy detour.

2. In 1993, Scottish cyclist Graeme Obree broke the World Hour Record on his home-made bicycle. What did he call his bike?

   a) *The Rocket*

   b) *Pedalo*

   c) *Old Faithful*

3. In the 2020 Giro d'Italia, EF Pro Cycling incurred a fine for "non-compliant clothing". In particular, what did their helmets depict?

   a) A googly-eyed emu

   b) A drunk-looking Martian

   c) A duck complete with bill

CYCLING WORDS

What do the following words mean?

1. À BLOC

a) Riding as hard as possible
b) Cycling in a close-knit group
c) Disc brake

2. BERM

a) Cycling in a crouched position
b) A banked turn
c) Heat exhaustion

3. CRACK

a) Time-trial specialist
b) To run out of energy or strength
c) Steep mountain track

4. FALSE FLAT

a) Deflated tyre caused by valve rather than puncture
b) A race which includes cobblestone roads
c) A deceptive low-gradient climb

HOW MANY?

How many letter C's are there on this page?

**Chuck and Cecelia quickly cycled
to the beach where they bought
chocolate ice creams.**

STAR NAME

The letters of the name of a well-known British cyclist have been spread evenly around the circle. Find the first letter in the cyclist's name and follow the letters, thereby completing the star – and the star's name. Who is the cyclist?

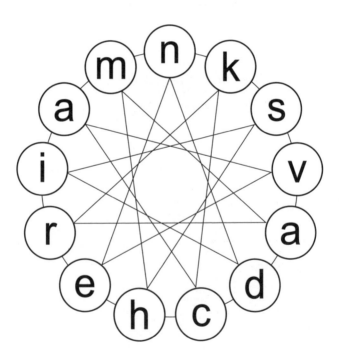

SPOT THE DIFFERENCE

Spot seven differences between the two pictures.

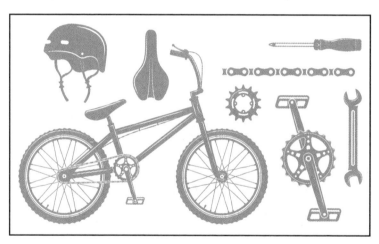

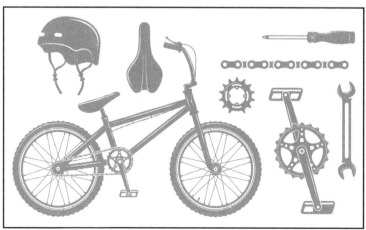

CODED CROSSWORD

Each letter of the alphabet has been replaced by a number. To solve the puzzle, you must decide which letter is represented by which number. To help you start, one of the words has been partly filled in. When you have solved the code, complete the bottom grid to discover a type of cycle race. What exactly is this?

	20		10		12		19		8		17		16	
1	3	20	5	3	21		15	18	3	4	12	21	7	16
	14		12		21		17		4		4		24	
6	12	7	4		12	20	20	4	15	25	24	23	3	4
	20		21		16							5		
19	3	3	18		1	3	12	4	21	2	4	3	12	22
	10		1		5		20		4		12			
8	3	4	15		3	4	7	16	12		16	12	6 F	3
			24		24		2		24		3		15 O	
12	10	16	3	4	21	12	7	24	10		16	15	4 R	22
	21								7		15		14	
1	12	24	23	20	3	2	12	4	10		25	24	7	21
	21		25		13		25		21		4		26	
11	25	12	21	4	12	7	24		15	9	10	21	3	4
	10		9		5		21		4		3		24	

1	2	3	4 R	5	6 F	7	8	9	10	11	12	13
14	15 O	16	17	18	19	20	21	22	23	24	25	26

22	3	7	4	7	24

MAZE

Time to enjoy a rather windy ride as you make your way from the start to a welcome cafe.

WORD SEARCH

Find all the following in the word search and the remaining letters will spell out something potentially useful. What is it?

Axle	Inner tube
Bar ends	Kickstand
Brake	Pedal
Cable	Rack
Cassette	Reflector
Chain	Rim
Cone	Spoke
Cup	Stem
Fork	Tyre
Frame	Valve
Handlebar	Wheel
Hub	

W	I	D	R	F	R	A	M	E	T	S
H	N	N	E	B	I	N	I	A	H	C
E	N	A	F	C	F	O	R	K	U	H
E	E	T	L	E	L	X	A	P	Y	U
L	R	S	E	C	L	R	A	C	K	B
E	T	K	C	A	S	S	E	T	T	E
V	U	C	T	P	E	D	A	L	P	C
A	B	I	O	Y	C	A	B	L	E	O
L	E	K	R	B	R	A	K	E	U	N
V	E	M	S	D	N	E	R	A	B	E
E	P	R	A	B	E	L	D	N	A	H

WHAT THEY SAID

The following quotes have some of their words missing. What did these people actually say?

1. Barry Hoban, British cyclist and multiple stage winner in the Tour de France, believed that

    "Merckx was the best because..."

    a) he had a voracious appetite for winning.
    b) he was the ultimate all-rounder.
    c) he had passion, instinct and exceptional skill.

2. What did American writer and traveller Jan Chipchase believe?

    "I find buying a bicycle is..."

    a) an investment in myself.
    b) the start of a new journey.
    c) a great way to stay in touch with people.

3. What does British cyclist and coach Sean Yates believe?

    "Good morale in cycling comes from good..."

    a) care of self and bike.
    b) training.
    c) legs.

MYSTERY SUDOKU

Complete the grid so that every row, column and 3 × 3 box contains the letters ADHINORTY in any order. One row or column contains a nine-letter word which is something important for cyclists to consider. What is it?

		D	A					R
	T	H		R				
			I	T		Y		A
							N	O
		R				T		
I	O							
N		O		H	I			
				D		N	Y	
H					N	R		

A PERPLEXING POSER

A cyclist was going down a street. She went past a stop sign without stopping, then turned left where there was a "No left turn" sign and went the wrong way down a one-way street. She passed a traffic policeman as she went. The policeman was on duty and the streets had not been closed off for a bike race. Everything was normal and as it should be, but the traffic policeman did not stop her. Why not?

DOUBLE TAKE

The words describing some parts of a bike have two different meanings, one for the bike part and another for something else. So, for example, the answer to the clue "lightning stroke (4)" would be "bolt". Solve the clue and name the bike part. The number of letters in the answer is given in brackets.

1. Pause (10)

2. Engross (4)

3. Stalk (4)

4. Eccentric (5)

5. Falsely incriminate (5)

6. Of little weight (5)

WORD LADDER

When out cycling, there are occasions when it is necessary to ring your bell and let others know your presence. In this word ladder, change one letter at a time to turn "ring" into "bell".

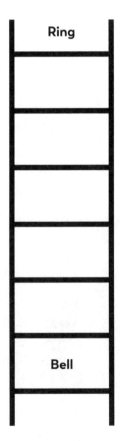

Ring

Bell

MYSTERY WORD SEARCH

Cycling offers many pleasures, but it can also have its hazards and mishaps. Six have been concealed in this word search. Discover what and where they are.

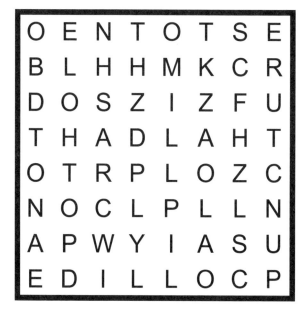

O	E	N	T	O	T	S	E
B	L	H	H	M	K	C	R
D	O	S	Z	I	Z	F	U
T	H	A	D	L	A	H	T
O	T	R	P	L	O	Z	C
N	O	C	L	P	L	L	N
A	P	W	Y	I	A	S	U
E	D	I	L	L	O	C	P

CRISS-CROSS: BIKE MAKES

All the following are names and makes of bike. Just as they have found their place in many a cycle shop, find a place for each in the grid.

3-letter name
BMC

4-letter names
Felt
Fuji
Ibis
Kona
Soma
Trek
Woom
Yeti

5-letter names
Focus
Ghost
Giant
Jamis
Marin
Niner
Norco
Salsa
Scott

6-letter names
Merida
Orange

7-letter names
Bianchi
Cervelo
Colnago
Devinci
Kestrel
Raleigh
Schwinn
Tommaso

8-letter names
Boardman
Brompton

9-letter names
Pinarello
Santa Cruz

10-letter names
Cannondale
Eddy Merckx

11-letter name
Specialized

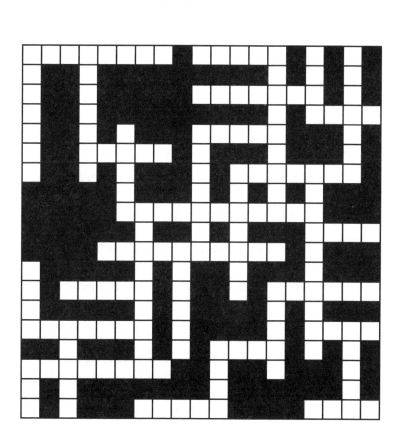

WORD BUILDER

The letters of a nine-letter word have been numbered 1 to 9. Solve the clues to discover what it is. The answer is an exciting and often significant feature of a race.

Letters 7, 4 and 9 give us a method

Letters 5, 3, 2 and 1 give us a pavement edge

Letters 7, 6, 2 and 9 are a sign of being cautious

Letters 4, 2, 3 and 8 give us a vicinity

Letters 1, 8, 5, 3 and 2 give us a bread maker

1	2	3	4	5	6	7	8	9

A PICTURE POSER

What bike part is suggested by the following?

CRYPTOGRAM

Solve the cryptogram to discover an interesting thought from bicycle designer Grant Petersen. To give you a start, Q = N, P = R and F = V.

H	Z	D	Q	S		M	U		W	D	E	J	E	C	G	O
			N													

V	O		P	D	L	G	V	W	C	G		V	P	H		H	Z	V	H
			R										R						

E	V	Q		B	N	O	H		V	W	M	N	H		O	V	F	G
		N															V	

H	Z	G		R	M	P	C	L
						R		

STRANGE BUT TRUE

What did Tsugunobu Mitsuishi accomplish in 1965?

a) He composed a ballet for cyclists. This was performed at the Korakuen Stadium, Tokyo, and shown live on Japanese television. It was so popular the ballet was performed again the following year.

b) He managed to remain motionless on a bicycle for over 5 hours.

c) He cycled across Japan on a unicycle.

d) He cycled up the fire escape of Japan's tallest building, a feat which took 1 hour 29 minutes.

WORD SEARCH: OLYMPIC AND PARALYMPIC MEDALLISTS

All the following cyclists have won gold in the Olympic or Paralympic Games. Seek out these champions in the grid – find them all and go for gold.

Armstrong	Meares
Boardman	Pendleton
Carrigan	Queally
Clancy	Rissveds
Cooke	Rowsell Shand
Cox	Storey
Cundy	Thomas
Fields	Trott
Hall	Turnham
Hoy	Vogel
Kenny	Vos
Manning	Wiggins

```
J W H X G R O C G N I N N A M E N
N P D Y A Y O A K C L A N C Y Q T
T S M O N X A R E V S T V S U G O
V U W H V M X M N V H O E E S S R
O S R I F C R S N M G R A T Y O S
F P O N G N V T Y E A L O K W L L
M S E V H G B R L E L R N S S F V
C D S N B A I O M Y E G E O G K R
A E D Q D L M N A Y C L X J I Y Z
R V L T O L S G S R L H C U N D Y
R S E A K L E I A S D K A D I X T
I S I Q C P Q T H L W M G L M X T
G I F Y O Y Z A O F R Y A U L L O
A R E F Z T N K G N I S B N N F R
N I J T L D Q N I F W S G Q W Z T
S A M O H T E O U O V B C O O K E
L D G N N N V H R I K I O N L I M
```

WORD LINK

Each of the three words in the clues below have a word in common. For example, if the clues were "count", "faith" and "weight", the answer would be "lose" (lose count, lose faith and lose weight). Answer each of the following clues correctly and an essential bike part will be revealed in the shaded column. What is it?

1. sell, option, drink
2. over, down, round
3. behind, away, close
4. limit, signal, being
5. secret, space, wide

1			
2			
3			
4			
5			

MINI SUDOKU: PRESTA

Many are familiar with the slender Presta valve, particularly as it is often used in road-style and mountain-bicycle inner tubes. In this mini sudoku, here's a chance to consider this valve in another way by completing the grid so that every row, column and 2 × 3 box contains the letters that make up "Presta".

T	S		A		
				T	
		A	P		R
			T	A	
	E	P			

FITTING WORDS

Fit the following words into the grid so that another word, which is something often fitted to bikes, is created in the shaded squares. What is it? To give you a start, letters in two of the words have already been entered.

BRAKE
FERRULE
GEARS
GUSSET
HYBRID
MITTS
PEDAL
SHIFTER

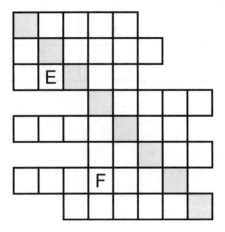

SPOT THE DIFFERENCE

Spot seven differences between the two pictures.

ANAGRAMS

Unscramble the following to reveal some types of bike, old and new.

1. MAD NET

2. I DO BRAKE!

3. OK IN MAIN TUBE

4. NUMBER ETC

5. THEN FRYING PAN

A PICTURE POSER

What style of racing is suggested by the following?

LETTER DROP

The letters in each of the columns need to be entered into the squares immediately below, but not necessarily in the same order. By placing the letters in the correct places you will reveal a thought from cycling legend Miguel Induráin. What did he say?

			N							
	E	H	Y		B	E	E	W		
	T	I	I	E	H	T	N	I	E	
	R	E	E	T	R	E	H	A	F	
M	P	O	F	M	T	E	Y	C	T	I	N
		,		■				■		
					.	■			■	
				■						
		,	■							

MAZE

Time for a cycle as you make your way from the top to the bottom. Enjoy the twists and turns. A-maze-ing stuff.

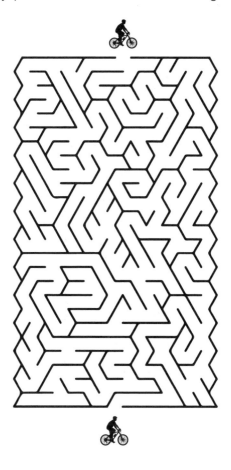

WORD LADDER

Competitive cyclists are always striving for a fast time. In this word ladder, changing one letter at a time, aim for a fast time as you turn "fast" into "time". On your marks...

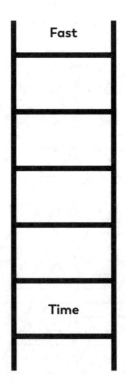

Fast

Time

WHAT THEY SAID

The following quotes have some of their words missing. What did these people actually say?

1. John Tomac, considered one of the greatest mountain bikers, said:

"It's hard to measure yourself if..."
   a) nobody is challenging you.
   b) you don't push yourself.
   c) you just take easy rides.

2. Laurent Jalabert, French cyclist and Vuelta a España winner, declared:

"The race is always won by a strongman. The truth comes through the..."
   a) pain.
   b) pedals.
   c) training.

3. Russell Mockridge, Australian cycling champion, had this to say:

"Before you can learn to win a race, ..."
   a) you've got to put in the miles.
   b) you've got to get your body position right.
   c) you have to learn to finish it.

CODED CROSSWORD

Each letter of the alphabet has been replaced by a number. To solve the puzzle, you must decide which letter is represented by which number. To help you start, one of the words has been partly filled in. When you have solved the code, complete the bottom grid to discover some advice given by cycling legend Eddy Merckx.

	25	22	17	17	5	18		23	10	12	4	2	18	
	7		3		2				11		10		13	
2	18	11	3	7	20	22		11	2	21	20	2	10	11
	17		10		10		18		13		16		5	
19	3 R	10 A	12 N	14	11	2	24	3	18		10	1	5	17
			14		7		21				18		23	
	19	24	18	11	2		3	2	10	14	18	11	17	3
	24				12		17		23				17	
24	12	20	5	17	18	10	13		24	5	20	17	3	
	21		17				17		12		3			
14	2	8	17		26	17	5	2	14	3	2	13	17	18
	25		25		10		6		10		15		17	
7	14	17	10	5	5	6		17	12	15	24	7	3	17
	17		3		26				20		17		7	
	3	17	14	17	17	13		9	17	11	11	5	17	

1	2	3 R	4	5	6	7	8	9	10 A	11	12 N	13
14	15	16	17	18	19	20	21	22	23	24	25	26

3	7	14	17		5	2	11	18

STAR NAME

The letters of the name of a well-known British cyclist and Olympic gold medallist have been spread evenly around the circle. Find the first letter in the cyclist's name and follow the letters, thereby completing the star – and the star's name. Who is the cyclist?

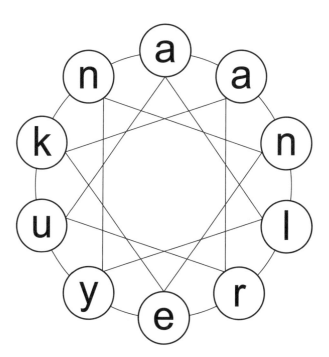

DOWN THE MIDDLE

Complete all the following words correctly and something potentially exciting will be revealed in the shaded squares. What is it? The answer is two words.

P	E		I	L
K	N		C	K
S	P		R	E
M	E		A	L
M	E		I	T
T	R		C	K
P	A		E	D
C	H		C	K

CROSS OUT

Cross out all the letters that appear more than once. The letters that are left, reading from top to bottom and left to right, will spell out part of a bike. What is it?

H	C	L	P	S	K	G	N
F	Q	I	M	A	J	D	V
O	U	Z	B	L	X	T	P
V	Z	G	F	A	Q	U	L
D	Y	X	O	I	M	C	J
K	H	S	R	B	E	Z	N

A PICTURE POSER

What are suggested by the following, which are found on some bikes?

MYSTERY SUDOKU

Complete the grid so that every row, column and 3 × 3 box contains the letters CELNORTUY in any order. One row or column contains a seven-letter word. When applied to cycling, what does this apt word mean?

T	L							
N			R			O		L
			E	N				
	R	U		C				
	T	Y		U	C			
			R		E	Y		
			O	Y				
R		Y		N			T	
						L	O	

CYCLING WORDS

What do the following words mean?

1. HAMMER

a) To be eliminated
b) To achieve a personal best
c) Riding fast in a bid to attack or break away from rivals

2. SKEWER

a) Rod mechanism that attaches a wheel to a bike
b) To skid
c) Failure to reach potential or race expectations

3. CADENCE

a) The degree of incline
b) Rate at which a cyclist pedals, measured in revolutions per minute
c) How much a cyclist leans when cornering

4. MUSETTE

a) Feed bag given to riders
b) Sweatband
c) Support bandage

CRYPTOGRAM

American actress Michelle Pfeiffer has starred in a great number of movies and, in her spare time, also enjoys her bike. To discover what she once said, solve the cryptogram. To give you a start, U = L, O = K and Z = P.

V		H	L	U	X	N		D	B		C	X	O	V	T	W		R	B
			L										K						

D	V	I	B	I	U	L		X	Z	X	H	C		X	T	Y
					L				P							

Z	K	C	C	V	T	W		V	C		D	X	I	O
P														K

C	F	W	L	C	Q	L	H		X	W	X	V	T

WORD SEARCH

All the following have won the Paris–Roubaix race. Find them in the grid and the remaining letters will reveal how author Iain MacGregor described the race.

Boonen

Cancellara

Coppi

Demol

Janssen

Kelly

Knaven

Leducq

Madiot

Merckx

Moser

Museeuw

O'Grady

Post

Raas

Rebry

Sagan

Tafi

Van Looy

```
K R E S O M T A H E T
O N U G H R N R E T S
I F A T T A E A R S A
Y P N V V A N L O O Y
R Q P E E S O L G P C
B C E O S N O E R X M
E U I N C S B C A K A
R D N C A Y N N D C D
K E L L Y G C A Y R I
L L O M E D A C J E O
I N G W U E E S U M T
```

A PERPLEXING POSER

It was a nice spring day and some cyclists decided to go for a ride. There were two cyclists in front of a cyclist, two cyclists behind a cyclist, and one cyclist in the middle. How many cyclists were going for a ride?

WHAT THEY SAID

The following quotes have some of their words missing. What did these people actually say?

1. What did cycling coach Chris Carmichael advise?

"Train your weakness..."

a) and practise.

b) and build up your skills.

c) and race your strength.

2. Having won and achieved so much in cycling, what was Geraint Thomas referring to?

"... you like nothing else."

a) Wind and rain test

b) A collision tests

c) Cobbles test

3. Complete cycling writer Owen Mulholland's thoughts:

"When we get into cycling, we inherit a point of view, a perception, ..."

a) an attitude toward life.

b) a chance to test ourselves.

c) a new energy.

WORD LADDER

There are many BMX riders who enjoy riding and performing tricks on flatland or flat ground. In this word ladder, enjoy some manoeuvring of a different kind as you change one letter at a time to turn the word "flat" into "land".

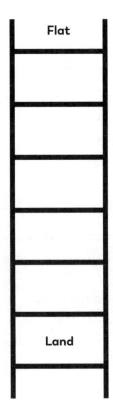

Flat

Land

ANAGRAMS

Unscramble the following to reveal some parts of a bike.

1. FLOWN THERE

2. AS KERB

3. OR SPOKEN IN FUSS

4. LEFT SCORER

5. A SHY ANTIC

MINI SUDOKU: HYBRID

Hybrid bikes are a popular choice for many, particularly as they combine the advantages of both road and mountain bikes. In this mini sudoku, complete the grid so that every row, column and 2 × 3 box contains the letters that make up "hybrid".

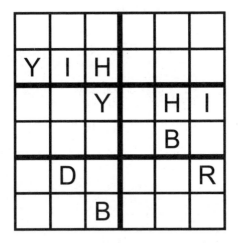

Y	I	H			
		Y		H	I
			B		
	D				R
		B			

WHO?

1. Who said, after winning his first cycling race, *"I won! I won! I don't have to go to school anymore"*?

2. Who was inspired to take up cycling after watching the BMX scenes in the film *E.T. the Extra-Terrestrial* and went on to become an Olympic champion?

3. Which member of The Beatles once had a dream of owning his own bike and was so pleased to finally get one that on *"the first night I even kept it in my bed"*?

4. Who was inspired to write the song "Bicycle Race" after watching a stage of the 1978 Tour de France? He was also lead singer in a major British rock group.

5. Who is often referred to by his first initial? He is a well-known British cyclist.

6. Who wrote, *"Get a bicycle. You will not regret it, if you live"*? He was an American writer and humourist.

CRISS-CROSS: VUELTA A ESPAÑA WINNERS

All the following have graced the podium by winning the Vuelta a España. See if you can find a rightful position for each in the grid.

3-letter name
Aru

4-letter names
Pino
Ruiz

5-letter names
Altig
Heras
Kelly
Yates
Zülle

6-letter names
Bracke
Deloor
Froome
Fuente
Horner
Merckx

Nibali
Roglic

7-letter names
Delgado
Gimondi
Hinault
Menchov
Pingeon
Ullrich

8-letter names
Anquetil
Contador
Quintana
Rominger
Valverde

9-letter name
Rodriguez

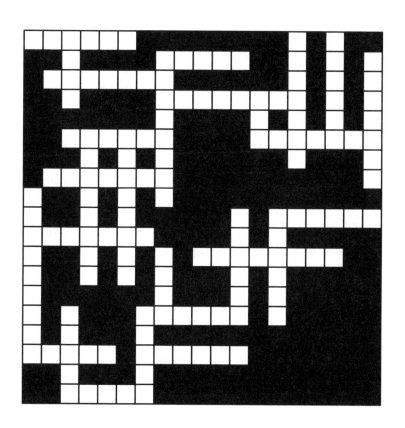

STRANGE BUT TRUE

Although finishing 50th in the 1956 Tour de France, Frenchman Roger Hassenforder received an especially loud round of applause when he took his lap of honour. Why?

a) After such a gruelling race, Hassenforder's bike was in a very poor state and just as he started the lap of honour he got a puncture. Exhausted and with his bike becoming increasingly difficult to ride, he wobbled round the circuit with the crowd cheering him on.

b) As he started his lap of honour, he unfurled a French flag that he had taken with him and waved it as he cycled along.

c) Famed for his antics, Hassenforder cycled his lap of honour backwards, sitting on the handlebars of his bike looking towards the saddle as he pedalled.

d) It was his 21st birthday and word had got out that Hassenforder had also just got engaged.

SPOT THE DIFFERENCE

Spot seven differences between the two pictures.

ACROSTICS

Solve the clues correctly and the shaded lines will reveal an important bike part. What is it?

1. Pursue
2. Salad vegetable
3. Citrus fruit
4. Sewing implement
5. Journey

1					
2					
3					
4					
5					

MYSTERY SUDOKU

Complete the grid so that every row, column and 3 × 3 box contains the letters ABEHINPRS in any order. One row or column contains a seven-letter word which relates to which cycling discipline?

	P				R			
					N	P	E	
E	B	A					R	
			B	H				I
	H	I				B	S	
P				R	S			
	A					N	H	E
	E	S	H					
			R				B	

CROSS OUT

Cross out all the letters that appear more than once. The letters that are left, reading from top to bottom and left to right, will spell out a bike part. What is it?

T	D	M	B	L	F	J	C
Q	H	E	K	V	A	U	N
J	Y	X	G	W	Z	Q	B
W	C	N	V	K	Y	D	H
X	A	R	F	L	I	T	M
K	D	P	Z	B	S	E	U

NICKNAMES

Many of the top cyclists have been given nicknames. See if you can match them up.

1. Marco Pantani	a) Le Monster
2. Graeme Obree	b) Monsieur Chrono
3. Greg LeMond	c) The Cannibal
4. Mark Cavendish	d) Il Elefantino
5. Jacques Anquetil	e) Big Mig
6. Cadel Evans	f) The Flying Scotsman
7. Miguel Induráin	g) The Professor
8. Eddy Merckx	h) The Badger
9. Chris Boardman	i) The Manx Missile
10. Bernard Hinault	j) Cuddles

WORD LINK

Each of the three words in the clues below have a word in common. For example, if the clues were "count", "faith" and "weight", the answer would be "lose" (lose count, lose faith and lose weight). Answer each of the following clues correctly to reveal a word in the shaded column, which is something found on a bike.

1. level, seller, Sunday
2. dream, down, cleaner
3. road, game, trial
4. double, charge, shape
5. end, fry, thought

1			
2			
3			
4			
5			

ANAGRAMS

Unscramble these anagrams to discover some top BMX tricks.

1. PHONY BUN

2. MEAN SPUR

3. NO NIGHT

4. RACY BAND

5. BEG A STAR

WORD SEARCH: BIKE PARTS

There are many parts to a bike, including some of the following. Seek them out in the grid.

Axle	Kickstand
Bar ends	Locknut
Bearing	Mudguard
Brake	Pannier
Cable	Pedal
Cassette	Rack
Chain	Reflector
Cogset	Rim
Coupler	Saddle
Derailleur	Seat post
Dynamo	Shifter
Ferrule	Spindle
Fork	Spoke
Frame	Stem
Gusset	Tyre
Handlebar	Valve
Headset	Wheel
Inner tube	Wingnut

```
H K P B Q N T U N K C O L K Z E E
A C S U Y M U D G U A R D P S T L
N A C H E B U T R E N N I A H T D
D R F E R R U L E R D T T N I E N
L D Y N A M O C S R I V U N F S I
E L D D A S W P E P F M N I T S P
B V W F Q D I L K R G S G E E A S
A R O W J L P P H G E N N R R C I
R R U M C U E N R A S L I N U D E
K D C E O E R K T O V A W R N U R
E S O C L O V P O V T H X A A P Y
M T G K L L O L W P E C T L M E T
A B S K N S I F A E S S E F E D B
R V E S T E M A L V K M E L B A C
F T T B R A K E R C B H X U F L J
G U S S E T T P I E H E A D S E T
S D N E R A B K F I D N I A H C R
```

LETTER DROP

The letters in each of the columns need to be entered into the squares immediately below, but not necessarily in the same order. By putting the letters in the correct places you will reveal an observation from cyclist and adventurer Scott Stoll.

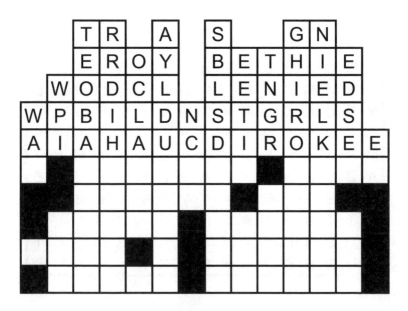

CYCLING WORDS

What do the following words or phrases mean?

1. FLAMME ROUGE

a) a flag raised to stop the race

b) a flag raised to indicate an infringement

c) a flag indicating there is one kilometre left to race

2. CASQUETTE

a) pouch worn around the waist

b) emergency puncture repair patch

c) cycling cap

3. ESPOIR

a) an independent rider in the Tour de France

b) age class for riders 19 to 22

c) service vehicle carrying spare bicycles or wheels

4. BAROUDEUR

a) a breakaway specialist

b) a race which includes cobblestone roads

c) a deceptive low-gradient climb

MINI SUDOKU: TANDEM

Riding a tandem can be great fun as well as being an efficient way to cycle. This mini sudoku gives you a chance to enjoy a tandem in another way by completing the grid so that every row, column and 2 × 3 box contains the letters that make up "tandem".

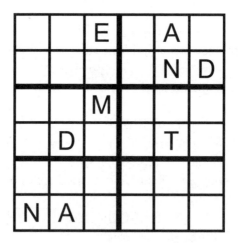

CODED CROSSWORD

Each letter of the alphabet has been replaced by a number. To solve the puzzle, you must decide which letter is represented by which number. To help you start, one of the words has been partly filled in. When you have solved the code, complete the bottom grid to discover something cyclists are pleased to achieve. What is it?

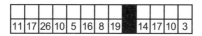

MAZE

Time for a cycle as you make your way from top to bottom.

WORD BUILDER

The letters of a nine-letter word have been numbered 1 to 9. Solve the clues to reveal an essential bike part. What is it?

Letters 5, 8, 3 and 6 give us something to cycle along

Letters 7, 6, 3 and 4 give us a curve

Letters 1, 2, 9 and 4 give us something difficult

Letters 2, 1, 6, 8 and 4 give us something out in front

Letters 7, 9, 6, 2 and 4 give us some staple food

1	2	3	4	5	6	7	8	9

CRYPTOGRAM

Solve the cryptogram to "enjoy" a cycling joke. The answer to the joke is in the answers. To give you a start, I = R and T = Y.

H	U	R	L	'	X		L	U	F		A	K	E	E	F	I	F	P	B	F
				'												R				

S	F	L	H	F	F	P		R		H	F	V	V	-	A	I	F	X	X	F	A
														-		R					

B	T	B	V	K	X	L		R	P	A		R		X	B	I	C	E	E	T

N	P	F		N	P		R		L	I	K	B	T	B	V	F	?
										R			Y				?

TAKE YOUR PICK

Which of the following is the correct answer? Take your pick.

1. Mountain biker Paul Roberts has enjoyed many a challenge, including taking part in 24-hour, non-stop mountain bike races as well as cycling the length of Great Britain, from Land's End to John o' Groats. However, in tackling many of these challenges, what does Paul carry on his back?

a) a spade
b) his trumpet (in a case)
c) an ironing board

2. Quite a few cyclists have cycled the length of Britain starting from Land's End, the most westerly point of mainland Cornwall, and finishing at John o' Groats in the very north of Scotland. In July 1886, George Mills successfully completed the journey on a penny-farthing but how long did he take?

a) 5 days, 1 hour and 45 minutes
b) 6 days, 2 hours and 12 minutes
c) 8 days, 10 hours and 55 minutes

3. In 1989, Greg LeMond won the Tour de France by the narrowest of margins. By how many seconds did he win the race?

a) Two seconds
b) Eight seconds
c) Thirteen seconds

A PERPLEXING POSER

After many weeks of practice Sara decided to enter a race. She did far better than she thought and was up with the leaders. As the finish approached, Sara made one final effort, overtaking the cyclist in second place. What position was Sara in now?

129

CROSS OUT

Cross out all the letters that appear more than once. The letters that are left, reading from top to bottom and left to right, will spell out something that many BMX riders enjoy. What is it?

O	F	B	U	E	C	W	D
Y	H	G	X	J	Q	I	T
Z	V	L	N	D	K	Y	H
E	W	I	T	X	B	O	V
Q	R	G	Z	U	Y	A	F
C	J	M	K	P	N	S	L

STAR NAME

The letters of the name of a well-known British cyclist have been spread evenly around the circle. Find the first letter in the cyclist's name and follow the letters, thereby completing the star – and the star's name. Who is the cyclist?

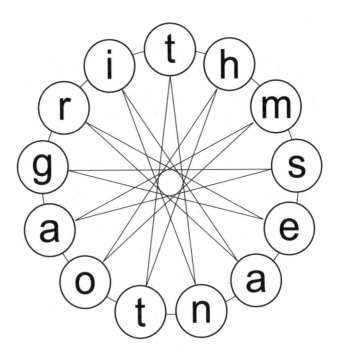

STRANGE BUT TRUE

In the 1890s, a six-day endurance event was held at New York's Madison Square Garden in which cyclists had to complete as many laps as possible. In order to keep going, cyclists kept their sleep and rest periods to a minimum. It was literally a test of endurance. In the event held in 1898, cyclist Charlie Miller was so far ahead of his rivals he was able to take a break from the race. What did he do?

a) He got married.

b) President William McKinley went to watch the event. Seeing the president, Charlie Miller got off his bike and spent an hour chatting to McKinley. The two men also enjoyed a drink together.

c) Being a keen singer, Miller gave an impromptu concert, inviting attendees to join in with some of the rousing songs he sang.

d) As the race coincided with his daughter's second birthday, he held a birthday party for her. Many of the spectators joined in with the celebrations, making the young girl's birthday all the more special. The staff of Madison Square Garden provided a cake.

WORD LADDER

The Milk Race, sponsored by the Milk Marketing Board, was held in Britain from 1958 to 1993 and was a major event in the sporting calendar. Often raced over two weeks, it attracted both amateur and professional riders and was watched by large crowds. In this word ladder, enjoy this early version of the Tour of Britain in another way as you change one letter at a time to turn the word "milk" into "race".

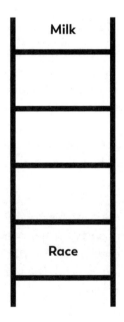

MYSTERY SUDOKU

Complete the grid so that every row, column and 3 × 3 box contains the letters ABCDEGINO in any order. One row or column contains an item (two words) found on some bikes. What is it?

I	O		N				A	
D				G			C	
A		G		O				N
				A	E			O
			O		C			
O			G	I				
E				D		N		B
	N			E				A
	D				N		O	C

CRISS-CROSS: WINNERS OF THE GRAND TOURS

All the following have won at least one of these races. Find a place for each in the grid.

4-letter names
Gaul
Maes
Pino
Riis
Ruiz
Thys

LeMond
Merckx
Nibali
Roglic
Sastre
Simoni
Thomas

5-letter names
Basso
Binda
Bobet
Evans
Heras
Roche
Yates
Zülle

7-letter names
Baldini
Bartali
Delgado
Hinault
Pantani
Ullrich

6-letter names
Bernal
Froome
Fuente
Horner
Leducq

8-letter names
Anquetil
Hesjedal
Induráin
Quintana

9-letter name
Rodriguez

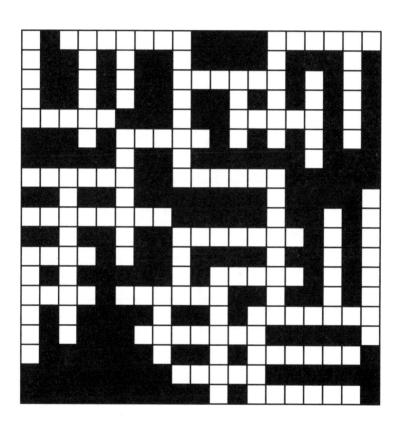

ACROSTICS

Solve the clues correctly and the shaded squares will reveal something that it is important for cyclists to get right. What is it?

1. Detective
2. Think highly of
3. Greek oracle site
4. Bold, adventurous
5. Duration
6. Accompany, bodyguard

1					
2					
3					
4					
5					
6					

WHAT THEY SAID

The following quotes have some of their words missing. What did these people actually say?

1. Eddy Merckx, who won so much, believed that

"The race is won by the rider..."

a) who knows his strengths.
b) who has most skill and luck.
c) who can suffer the most.

2. Greg LeMond, American cyclist and two-time winner of the Road Race World Championship, said of mountain biking,

"It's my kind of sport – hard, individualistic, and..."

a) bruising.
b) not a lot of tactics.
c) great scenery.

3. Missy Giove, American downhill mountain biker and a downhill world champion, declared,

"It's our job as riders to keep..."

a) this a soul sport.
b) this a sport of thrills.
c) this a sport for all.

MYSTERY WORD SEARCH

Find the elusive cyclist. There is only one in the grid but just where is that "cyclist"?

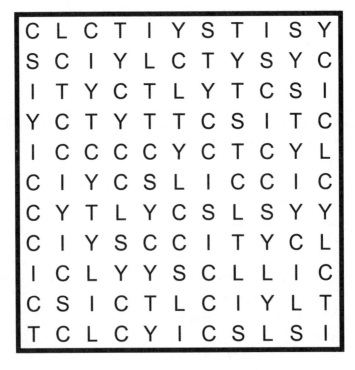

```
C L C T I Y S T I S Y
S C I Y L C T Y S Y C
I T Y C T L Y T C S I
Y C T Y T T C S I T C
I C C C C Y C T C Y L
C I Y C S L I C C I C
C Y T L Y C S L S Y Y
C I Y S C C I T Y C L
I C L Y Y S C L L I C
C S I C T L C I Y L T
T C L C Y I C S L S I
```

SURPRISE PRIZE

In addition to the pleasure of competing, some races also reward the winner with an unusual prize. See if you can successfully match the race to the bizarre prize.

1. Kuurne–Brussels–Kuurne   a) bananas

2. Paris–Roubaix   b) piglet

3. Tour of Turkey   c) stuffed donkey

4. Tro-Bro Léon   d) bucket of gravel

5. Uno-X Development Weekend   e) barrel of beer

6. The BinckBank Tour   f) mounted cobblestone

ON TRACK

Find the start, then moving one letter at a time – either horizontally, vertically or diagonally – discover something that some cyclists use and value. What is it? The answer is two words.

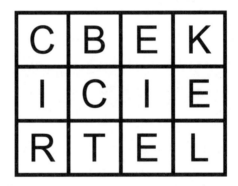

C	B	E	K
I	C	I	E
R	T	E	L

TAKE YOUR PICK

Which of the following is the correct answer? Take your pick.

1. What was the Dudafoon, invented by Godfried-Willem Raes?

   a) An electroacoustic sculptural instrument which used a bicycle wheel. Sounds and frequencies made by the spokes were picked up and amplified.

   b) A lightweight structure which went over a bike, protecting the cyclist from the elements. It was effective, provided the weather was not too windy.

   c) A bicycle mounted on floats. Raes was a keen fisherman and, to ensure he was not restricted to the river bank, he mounted his bike on floats. This allowed him to cycle out on the river to fish. He may have caught fish but his invention did not catch on.

2. In 2012, Sun Chao from north-east China spent four months building a fully functional bicycle. What did he make it from?

   a) Bamboo garden canes
   b) Plastic straws
   c) Lollipop sticks

3. Which country in 2010 pioneered the ECO Cycle, an underground storage facility for parking bikes?

   a) Netherlands
   b) Singapore
   c) Japan

MINI SUDOKU: GRINDS

Many a BMX rider enjoys performing grinds, especially as there are lots of different variations to try. In this mini sudoku, complete the grid so that every row, column and 2 × 3 box contains the letters that make up "grinds".

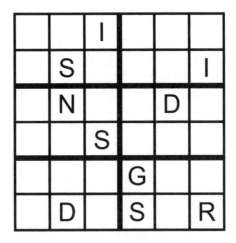

STRANGE BUT TRUE

What mishap befell British cyclist Pat Boyd when he entered a kermesse, a road race, in Belgium in the early 1950s?

a) While cycling by a river, he sustained a puncture. As he pulled off the road, his bike tumbled down the river bank and he tumbled down too. Both ended up in the river with Boyd, minus bike, being rescued by onlookers.

b) Having lost time due to a puncture, Boyd caught up with a Belgian cyclist who knew the local area. The Belgian suggested a shortcut down a passage. On seeing the peloton, Boyd cycled furiously and managed a top-ten finish. Unfortunately, the race the two had joined turned out to be a different one and so Boyd's efforts counted for nothing.

c) Having raced well, Boyd made a determined effort as the finish came into sight. As he cycled furiously over the wet cobbles, he skidded and went straight into a television camera crew who were recording the event. It made great action footage.

LETTER DROP

The letters in each of the columns need to be entered into the squares immediately below, but not necessarily in the same order. By placing the letters in the correct places, you will reveal an interesting thought from American cyclist John Howard.

	A		S		C	G				
	E		B	E	R	E	G	R	E	
V	E	H	C	I	E	I	E	I	I	E	I
P	A	S	I	U	L	Y	O	U	N	I	S
T	H	I	T	S	C	N	N	C	L	S	T	S	S

X

Something many BMX riders enjoy is hidden in the shaded squares. Insert the following words in the correct position to discover what lies hidden in the X. To give you a start, some letters have been entered in the grid.

ANSWER

FRIEND

GADGET

HURDLE

ITALIC

SKATER

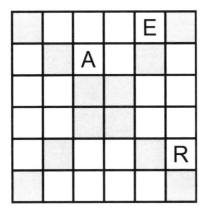

SPOT THE DIFFERENCE

Spot seven differences between the two pictures.

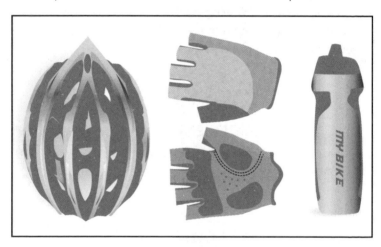

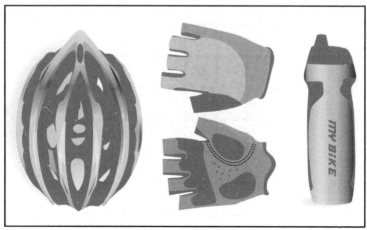

WORD BUILDER

Letters spelling out two words have been numbered 1 to 9. Solve the clues to reveal something that many people enjoy following. What is it?

Letters 6, 3 and 1 give us a label

Letters 9, 7, and 5 give us something to fish with

Letters 2, 7, 6 and 3 give us a roster

Letters 4, 7, 8, 1, 3 and 6 give us a chewy sweet

Letters 5, 9, 3, 1, 7 and 4 give us a mythical monster

1	2	3	4	5	6	7	8	9

CROSSWORD

Solve the clues and in the shaded squares you will discover the surprise leader of the 1997 Critérium International race in France. The answer is two words.

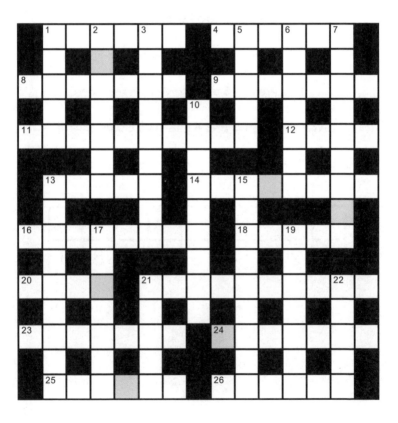

Across

1 Sponsor (6)
4 Decorative pin (6)
8 Let the air out (7)
9 Before now (7)
11 Called The Cannibal (4,6)
12 Unfortunately (4)
13 Sag (5)
14 Elated, over the moon (8)
16 Theatrical (8)
18 Bike part transferring power from pedals to drive-wheel (5)
20 Slightly open (4)
21 First American to win the Tour de France (4, 6)
23 Based on experience (7)
24 Sports ground (7)
25 Tension (6)
26 Emergency (6)

Down

1 Beg (5)
2 Hunting cry (5-2)
3 At the scene (2-3-4)
5 Take it easy (5)
6 Culinary herb (7)
7 Handy trio (anag) (9)
10 Gave harsh shrill cry (9)
13 Help riders become airborne (4, 5)
15 Embezzler (9)
17 More jolly (7)
19 Naval fleets (7)
21 Handlebar parts (5)
22 Naming words (5)

WORD LADDER

In many a race, top cyclists hold back until the right moment to challenge for the lead. In this word ladder, hold back no longer and, changing one letter at a time, turn "hold" into "back".

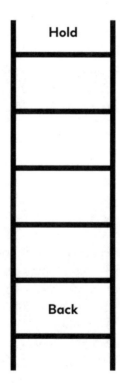

CROSS OUT

Cross out all the letters that appear more than once. The letters that are left, reading from top to bottom and left to right, will spell out a discipline in a form of cycling. What is it?

N	P	U	D	B	Y	O	W
A	X	F	Q	L	S	Z	G
M	K	V	H	I	U	P	J
Z	C	G	L	O	A	X	K
B	N	Q	E	D	Y	R	F
J	I	S	W	C	T	M	H

ANAGRAMS

Unscramble the following to reveal some parts of a bike.

1. RIDES BACK

2. IDEAL RULER

3. TWIN GUN

4. PEN LIDS

5. MANY DO

MYSTERY SUDOKU

Complete the grid so that every row, column and 3 × 3 box contains the letters ADEILMNOS in any order. One row or column contains a seven-letter word related to cycling. What does this word mean?

						N	E	L
I			M	L				A
			E				M	
D					N	E		
		L	D		I	S		
		S	L					I
	S				M			
O				I	L			S
A	D	I						

TRAIL FINDER

The British Isles have many fine cycling trails, but where are the following located? Match the trail to its location.

1. Camel

2. Red Squirrel

3. Tarka

4. Cuckoo

5. Crab and Winkle Way

6. Kingfisher

7. Brunel

8. Phoenix

9. Rodwell

a) Kent

b) Sussex

c) Northern Ireland and Republic of Ireland

d) Oxford and Buckinghamshire

e) Pembrokeshire

f) Isle of Wight

g) Dorset

h) Devon

i) Cornwall

WORD LINK

Each of the three words in the clues below have a word in common. For example, if the clues were "count", "faith" and "weight", the answer would be "lose" (lose count, lose faith and lose weight). Answer each of the following clues correctly to reveal an important bike part in the shaded column.

1. sky, point, time
2. won, blow, carry
3. start, off, cold
4. shoes, surface, social
5. test, history, pencil

1			
2			
3			
4			
5			

CRISS-CROSS: RACE ACROSS AMERICA

The Race Across America has been called "The World's Toughest Bicycle Race" and is one of the longest endurance events in the world. All the following have triumphed. Find places for them all in the map.

4-letter names
Chew
Kish
Wyss

5-letter names
Boyer
Robic
Solon

6-letter names
Larsen
Schoch
Tatrai
Zotter

7-letter names
Fourney
Secrest

8-letter names
Bischoff
Fasching
Haldeman
Spilauer
Strasser

9-letter name
Penseyres

13-letter name
Clavadetscher

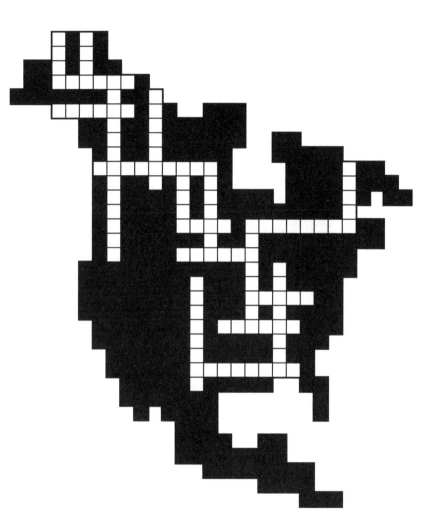

A PICTURE POSER

What is suggested by the following?

HIDDEN PARTS

In each of the sentences below, a bike part is hidden. For instance, in the sentence "I hurried home to watch Aintree racing", the word "chain" is hidden in wat**ch Ain**tree.

1. Either put the spare batteries on the shelf or keep them in the drawer.

2. I saw how he elegantly rode his bike down the road.

3. It's a pity, really, that more people did not see the final sprint.

4. He was poker-faced when he fell off his bike.

5. When she first embarked on the tour she did not know how demanding it would be.

ON THE RIGHT TRACK

Something that does good and could also make you feel good has been entered into the grid. Starting with the circled letter and moving one letter at a time, either horizontally, vertically or diagonally, discover what it is. The answer is three words.

LETTER DROP

The letters in each of the columns need to be entered into the squares immediately below, but not necessarily in the same order. By placing the letters in the correct places, you will reveal some tactical advice given by Eddy Merckx. What did he say?

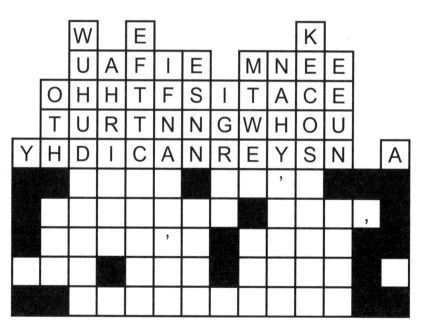

ACROSTICS

Solve the clues correctly and the shaded squares will reveal something that many BMX riders appreciate. What is it?

1. Pointed
2. Destiny, fate
3. Following
4. Cogitate
5. Ways out

1				
2				
3				
4				
5				

STRANGE BUT TRUE

Beryl Burton is known as one of the cycling greats. Strong and talented, this Yorkshire lady not only broke many records but also won two world Road Race World Championships and five world pursuit titles. She also believed that "Anything lads can do, I can do," and frequently proved this.

On one occasion Beryl took part in the Otley Cycle Club 12-hour time trial. Although the men started first, Beryl overtook them all, including the celebrated Mike McNamara, who himself was on course to set a new men's record that day. As she overtook Mike McNamara what did she do?

a) She gave him a crunchy oatmeal biscuit, one that she had baked the day before.

b) Being meticulous in her preparation for races, Beryl always carried several tyre patches "just in case". As she passed McNamara, she handed him a tyre patch "just in case".

c) She gave him a liquorice allsort.

d) She called over "I'll buy you a pint of beer at the finish," which she did. A picture of the two cyclists enjoying a celebratory pint appeared in many of the newspapers the next day.

WORD SEARCH: BMX TRICKS

There are a great many BMX tricks to master and have fun with, including some of the following. See if you can find them in the grid.

Backflip	Invert
Barspin	Lookback
Bar Turn	Nac Nac
Bunny Hop	No Foot
Candy Bar	Nollie
Crankflip	Nose Pivot
Crooked	Nothing
Crossfoot	Superman
Decade	Tabletop
Drop	Tailwhip
Fakie	Toboggan
Feeble	Tri Star
Flair	Truckdriver
Full Cab	Turndown
Grizzly	Wallride
Icepick	

```
B N I P S R A B W K R P X K U B J
D F B E N O N G F A O E R G P A C
E A G A G J R F Z T L H H I K R S
C K G R D I U U E N O L L I E T N
A I Y R Z E J L T G O F R U G U T
D E O Z Y G B L F K K T X I T R R
E P L Q S A D C F C B D H P D N U
C Y T B T U U A L A E E I O E C
N R O R E B P B Y A C K N L N F K
W R O U I E B E Z B K O O F P G D
O I G S S F U R U J O S K I I R
D A U O S Y T T N M X R E N H C I
N L P L X F N A C N A C P A W E V
R F T O O F O N R H Y N I R L P E
U T R E V N I O P L M H V C I I R
T O B O G G A N T Q L M O Q A C B
E R A B Y D N A C G R U T P T K J
```

MAZE

Time for a mountain trail. Find your way along the tracks until you get to the centre – a good place to stop for a drink.

MISSING PART

Insert the name of a bike part so that, reading down, five five-letter words are formed. What is the bike part?

S	E	H	A	A
O	N	A	G	P
I	M	O	N	I
D	Y	C	T	L

WHAT THEY SAID

The following quotes have some of their words missing. What did the following actually say?

1. What did American author James E. Starrs think?

   "... is incompatible with bicycling."

   a) Lethargy
   b) Boredom
   c) Melancholy

2. In the early days of cycling, Albert A. Pope, founder of the Columbia Bicycle Company, described the bicycle as

   "An ever-saddled horse..."

   a) which is ever-ready to take you places.
   b) which is easier to ride.
   c) which eats nothing.

3. In describing Tour de France winner Jacques Anquetil, French sports journalist and Tour de France director Jacques Goddet wrote:

   "He blended with his bicycle like a..."

   a) rider with his horse.
   b) musician with his instrument.
   c) batsman and his bat.

WORD LADDER

When out cycling there always comes a time when you need to slow down and come to a stop. Similarly, in preparing for certain BMX tricks, slowing down at just the right moment is essential. This word ladder gives you a chance to slow down in another way. Change one letter at a time to turn "slow" into "down" and, with speed not of the essence, you can take your time.

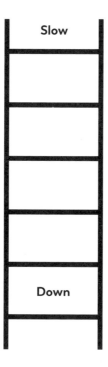

Slow

Down

CRISS-CROSS: SANTOS TOUR DOWN UNDER

This popular race was first held in 1999 and takes place in and around Adelaide, South Australia. All the following have been overall winners, including in the Women's Tour Down Under. Find places for them all in the grid.

5-letter names
Davis
Impey
Meyer
Porte

6-letter names
Dennis
Jonker
O'Grady
Rogers
Spratt
Winder

7-letter names
Elmiger
Garfoot
Gerrans
Greipel
Maignan
Sanchez
Slagter

9-letter name
Astarloza

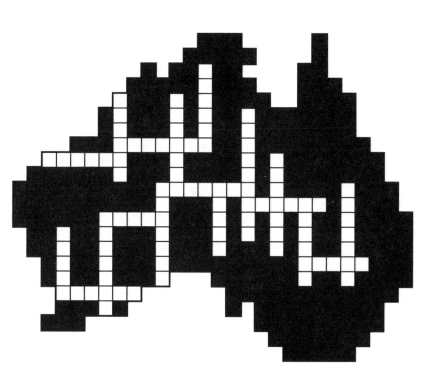

FITTING WORDS

A practice that has been illicitly used in cycling has been hidden in the shaded squares. Insert the following words in the correct position to discover what it is. To give you a start, some letters have been entered in the grid. What does this practice involve?

CLOCKS
EMPLOY
GUITAR
OUTCRY
STUPOR
SUPERB

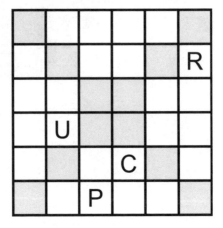

BIKE PARTS MEDLEY

The names of two bike parts have been merged together. The letters are in the correct order and the words are of equal length. Can you separate the two parts and determine what they are?

1. FWRAHEMELE

2. CAPBELDAEL

3. SVAPLOVKEE

4. CBHARIAKNE

169

ANAGRAM CHALLENGE

IRK PIRATE

This is an anagram of something almost all cyclists have. Once you solve this, these other anagrams should be easier to solve.

1. TRY THE CAP

2. SET REVELRY

3. I'VE SHADE

4. SPARED NAP

MYSTERY SUDOKU

Complete the grid so that every row, column and 3 × 3 box contains the letters DEHILNOPS in any order. One row or column contains a seven-letter name of a bike part. What is it?

	L						O	D
	O				I			
I	D				H		L	P
					D		N	H
		O				L		
H	S		I					
O	H		E				D	L
			S				I	
S	P						H	

A PERPLEXING POSER

A cyclist was enjoying a ride one Sunday afternoon. After passing through a village and heading down a country lane, she came to a junction where the lane split into four. Annoyingly, the signpost had been knocked down. Without a map, phone or anyone to ask, the cyclist needed to know the correct way to go. With the signpost lying on the ground, how did the cyclist sort the problem out and continue her journey?

LETTER DROP

The letters in each of the columns need to be entered into the squares immediately below, but not necessarily in the same order. By putting the letters in the correct places you will reveal a quote from American cyclist Frank McCormack.

		I			E					
	L	O	T	A	K	T	L		U	
I	L	B	K	E	A	B	D		G	S
M	Y	P	T	S	T	L	N	O	E	A	O
F	A	S	I	R	S	I	E	S	A	S	S	E

SPOT THE DIFFERENCE

Spot seven differences between the two pictures.

WORD BUILDER

The letters of something potentially exciting and challenging have been numbered 1 to 9. Solve the clues to discover what it is. The answer is two words.

Letters 6, 7 and 3 give us a wheel edge

Letters 5, 4 and 8 give us something to drink

Letters 8, 2 and 3 give us an objective

Letters 9, 7, 3, 2 and 1 give us a boundary

Letters 3, 4, 6, 2 and 5 give us excellence and something you earn through good work, which is applicable if you have solved the puzzle!

1	2	3	4	5	6	7	8	9

CRYPTOGRAM

Solve the cryptogram to discover a quotation from Lord Charles Beresford and something many will agree with. To give you a start, O = V, M = K and A = M.

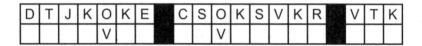

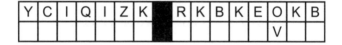

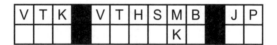

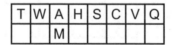

MINI SUDOKU: TRAILS

There are an ever-increasing number of cycle and mountain trails for cyclists to enjoy. Here's a chance to enjoy trails in another way by completing the grid so that every row, column and 2 × 3 box contains the letters that make up the word "trails".

R					
	S	A			
I			T		
	L				R
			A	S	
			T		

WORD LADDER

The Nosepick is an impressive but challenging BMX trick calling for good balance. In this word ladder, take up another challenge and, by changing one letter at a time, turn "nose" into "pick".

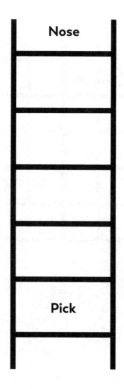

Nose

Pick

A PICTURE POSER

What is suggested by the following? Sorry.

ACROSTICS

Solve the clues correctly and the shaded columns will reveal an important bike part. What is it?

1. Container for liquid
2. Rue
3. Busy
4. Dog house
5. Repeat performance

1					
2					
3					
4					
5					

FIND THE PUNCTURE

A puncture is not always easy to find so here is a chance to put your skills to the test to see if you can find two punctures hidden in the word search.

```
            C U T
          P R N N P U N
        P C R C U R C P U E U
      N U N U T E C R U P N P E
    U P C P T P R E T U C R N P U
    R C R N U E T P R N R U N R P
  P U N C T P P T E U T U R T P E U
  T U P R P U R N P T N P E N R U T
E P E R E U N R T R E R C U P C T R C
R C N P C E C P N U R T R T N C N C E
R P C C T U T C R U N U C R U N E T U
  N U E C N U C E N P U U U N R N E
  U C N R P R P U P U T R T P N E U
    E U P N E N E E T R C N U C P
    C R U U E U E C E P R T C T U
      E R P R C T P R T U N P P
      U E U T P U T P C T U
        U P E N E N R
            N E P
```

TAKE YOUR PICK

Which is the correct answer to these questions? Take your pick.

1. During his long career, Mario Cipollini enjoyed 191 victories and in 2002 was World Champion. However, the Italian road cyclist often found himself being fined. Why?
    a) He wore extravagant skin suits.
    b) He hated the "media circus" and did not attend some of the obligatory press conferences.
    c) He frequently ridiculed the petty restrictions that race organizers placed on competitors and, by speaking out, was in contravention of some of the rules he found so objectionable.

2. Despite having taken the lead in the 1947 Tour de France, French cyclist Louison Bobet refused to wear the yellow jersey. Why?
    a) He did not like the material.
    b) He always considered yellow an unlucky colour.
    c) He did not want to be conspicuous and "stand out like a sore thumb".

3. Although he had won the Giro d'Italia in 1925, 1927, 1928 and 1929, why did Alfredo Binda not compete in the 1930 Giro?
    a) He had become such a celebrity he was busy making a film about himself – something he enjoyed and also found more lucrative!
    b) He was paid to stay away.
    c) A threat had been made on his life. A rival was later found responsible, jailed and banned from the sport.

182

A PERPLEXING POSER

It may be made for two but there is only one in a tandem.
A bicycle too has another one,
but a recumbent has two.

What is this referring to?

CYCLING WORDS

What do the following cycling words mean?

1. MUUR
a) To finish last in a race
b) Race medic
c) A short, steep climb

2. SQUIRREL
a) Unstable cyclist who cannot maintain a steady line or speed
b) To withdraw from a race
c) Racing cyclist who holds back behind the leader until the last moment

3. STAGIAIRE
a) Preliminary or practice race
b) Amateur cyclist riding for a professional team for a trial period
c) Sprint specialist

4. ROULEUR
a) Race marshal
b) Cyclist who goes well on flat and undulating terrain
c) Route sheet given to competitors

WORD LINK

Each of the three words in the clues below have a word in common. For example, if the clues were "count", "faith" and "weight", the answer would be "lose" (lose count, lose faith and lose weight). Answer each of the following clues correctly to reveal a word in the shaded column, which is an important part of a bicycle.

1. pay, away, hold
2. wood, sure, keen
3. talk, food, cry
4. ahead, rank, apart
5. order, safe, away

1			
2			
3			
4			
5			

CROSSWORD

Solve the clues and the shaded squares will reveal a word used in cycling. What exactly is it?

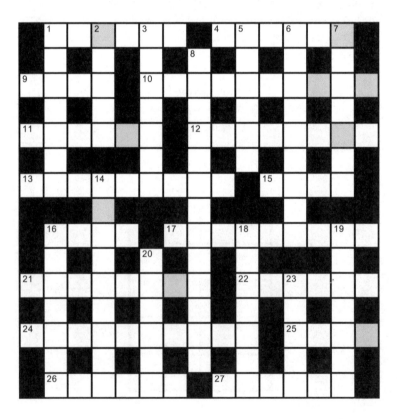

Across

1 Scrape (anag) (6)

4 The _____, nickname of Bernard Hinault (6)

9 Utensil found on bike? (4)

10 Writer (10)

11 Overlooked (6)

12 Significant feature or event (8)

13 Broken rock used for repairing or making roads (4, 5)

15 Advantage (4)

16 Sprint (4)

17 Propelling a bicycle (9)

21 Bend over (with laughter or pain) (6, 2)

22 Schrader, Presta (examples) (6)

24 Athletes' headpieces (10)

25 Tranquil (4)

26 Gives way (6)

27 Boring tools (6)

Down

1 Condition (7)

2 Pastries (5)

3 To re-examine (7)

5 Canopy (6)

6 Winner's award (4,5)

7 Hold back for future use (7)

8 Famous cycling race (6, 1, 6)

14 Stopping mechanism on some bikes (4, 5)

16 Entrance (7)

18 Mentor (7)

19 Sewing implements (7)

20 Ocean floor (6)

23 Nearby (5)

ANAGRAMS

Unscramble the following to reveal some parts of a bike.

1. EARNS BIG

2. RAGES

3. KEPT CROSS

4. ACE HINTS

5. TESTS ACE

LETTER DROP

The letters in each of the columns need to be entered into the squares immediately below, but not necessarily in the same order. By putting the letters in the correct places you will reveal a thought from British cyclist Sarah Bentley.

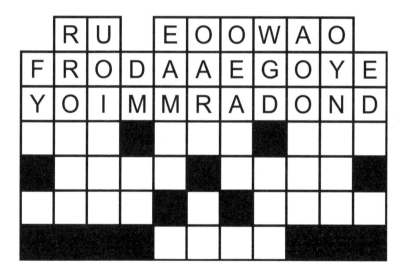

MINI SUDOKU: LIGHTS

Time for a bit of illumination. In this mini sudoku, complete the grid so that every row, column and 2 × 3 box contains the letters that make up the word "lights".

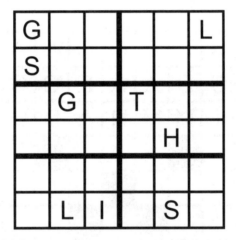

MISSING PART

Insert the name of a bike part so that, reading down, five five-letter words are formed. What is the bike part?

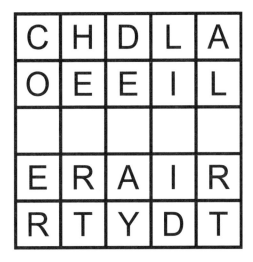

C	H	D	L	A
O	E	E	I	L
E	R	A	I	R
R	T	Y	D	T

WHAT THEY SAID

The following quotes have some of their words missing. What did these people actually say?

1. What did Scottish cyclist David Millar write?

"The first time I rode a bike I was four or five. ..."

a) I couldn't work the brakes so I went a long way.

b) I knew then I wanted to be a cyclist.

c) I crashed into the back of a car.

2. What did American cycling expert and engineer Fred DeLong think?

"Cycling is the sport..."

a) of pedalling.

b) open to everyone.

c) of usefulness.

3. What did Spanish cyclist and five-time Tour de France winner Miguel Induráin believe?

"My strength was that I am more balanced..."

a) and calmer than most other riders.

b) and had great reserves of energy.

c) and a great tactician.

A PERPLEXING POSER

Some friends decided to have a bike race.
Although Maria led most of the way she did not win.
Jess, who had put in a lot of practice, did not win either.
Terri had hoped to do better and came in after Charlie.
Eduardo raced well but did not finish ahead of Jess.
He also did not finish in either the fourth
or fifth position in the race.
Maria did not finish in front of Terri.

In what order did the friends finish?

CRYPTOGRAM

Paul de Vivie, who wrote as Vélocio, was publisher of *Le Cycliste* and inspired the French nation with his passion for cycling and the benefits it can bring. Solve the cryptogram to discover some of his words. To give you a start, C = F and E = G.

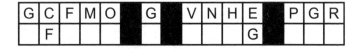

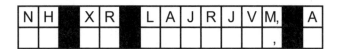

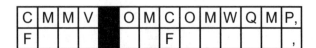

WORD BUILDER

The letters of what can be an important part of a bike have been numbered 1 to 9. Solve the clues to discover what it is and possibly have a think about it.

Letters 3, 5, 2 and 7 give us pedal pushers

Letters 1, 8, 4 and 5 give us a part to play

Letters 6, 8, 9 and 5 give us the centre of an apple

Letters 3, 4, 8, 1, 2 and 7 give us a piece of broccoli

1	2	3	4	5	6	7	8	9

CROSS OUT

Cross out all the letters that appear more than once. The letters that are left, reading from top to bottom and left to right, will spell out a type of bike and a type of cycling. What is it?

B	H	F	L	J	G	D	M
U	R	Q	C	W	T	K	O
V	A	X	Y	B	Z	G	S
F	W	K	T	H	R	V	U
X	E	P	Q	C	J	A	D
M	Z	O	I	L	Y	N	E

MYSTERY SUDOKU

Complete the grid so that every row, column and 3 × 3 box contains the letters ABDEILNRS in any order. One row or column contains an accessory fitted on some bikes. The answer is seven letters and consists of two words. What is it?

R		B				D		N
	I				N			
L	N				S	A		
				N	D			
	L	S				R	D	
			S	L				
		N	B				E	R
			I				N	
D		E				I		S

ANAGRAMS

Unscramble the following to reveal some tools.

1. PENS RAN

2. PERILS

3. KEEN ALLY

4. YEP, CUP CLIMB!

5. CHECK NEW SORT

FITTING WORDS

Fit the following words into the grid so that two words, which represent something that can be exciting, are created in the shaded squares. What are they? To give you a start, some of the letters have been entered in the grid.

ASCEND
CORNER
HELMET
SCRUFF
SKIING
SPRAIN

CRISS-CROSS: THE GREATS

Over the years so many have contributed to cycling and helped make it the exciting sport and activity it has become. Below are some of those who have made a difference and achieved greatness. Find places for them all in the grid.

3-letter names
Hoy
Vos

4-letter name
Hill

5-letter names
Binda
Cooke
Coppi
Kelly
Kenny
Longo
Obree
Roche
Yates

6-letter names
Boonen
Burton
Froome
LeMond

Millar
Storey
Thomas

7-letter names
Deignan
Hinault
Simpson
Wiggins

8-letter names
Anquetil
Boardman
Induráin

9-letter names
Cavendish
Pendleton

10-letter names
Brailsford
Cancellara

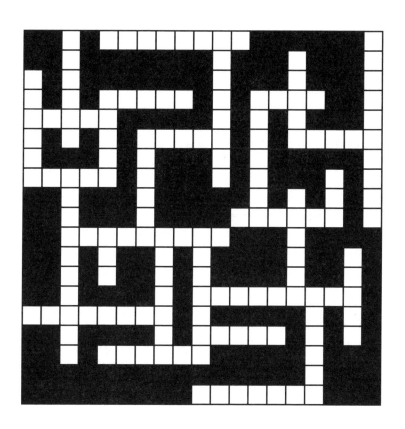

STRANGE BUT TRUE

As we near the end of this book, let's turn our attention to what happened near the end of the 2004 Milan–San Remo race. German cyclist Erik Zabel was close to winning the race for the fifth time, but what denied him victory?

a) At the pivotal moment, Zabel turned round to see how much lead he had and lost momentum.

b) As he neared the finish, he raised his arms in victory and was pipped at the post.

c) A spectator dropped an empty drink can which rolled on the track. A slight swerve to avoid the can cost Zabel the race.

d) In the final moments, Zabel got a fly in his mouth causing him to cough, become distracted and get overtaken.

BETWEEN THE WHEELS

Well done for reaching the end and I hope you enjoyed the puzzles you tackled. For the last one, an eight-letter word can be inserted between the wheels so that, reading downward, eight three-letter words can be formed. What is the word? You can be proud.

ANSWERS

1. Anagrams
1 seat post, 2 inner tube,
3 pedals, 4 handlebars,
5 headlight

2. Take Your Pick
1b (the company involved was
the Coventry Sewing Machine
Company), 2c, 3c

3. Mystery Sudoku

M	E	I	L	S	H	A	C	O
S	L	O	A	E	C	I	H	M
C	H	A	M	O	I	S	L	E
L	C	S	E	H	M	O	I	A
O	A	E	C	I	L	H	M	S
I	M	H	S	A	O	C	E	L
H	I	M	O	L	S	E	A	C
A	O	C	I	M	E	L	S	H
E	S	L	H	C	A	M	O	I

4. Cycling Words
1b, 2a, 3c, 4c

5. Cross Out
BMX

6. Cryptogram
We use it for transportation,
sport, recreation, and make it
a way of life.

7. Word Search: Bike Parts

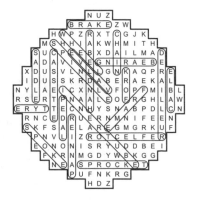

8. A Riddle
Gears

9. Spot the Difference
See the solution at the end
of this section.

10. Crossword
Across: 1 puncture, 5 brakes,
9 simplify, 10 glance, 11 eclipsed,

12 banned, 14 stabiliser,
18 concurring, 22 sprint,
23 donation, 24 ordeal,
25 airborne, 26 saddle,
27 agonised.
Down: 1 passed, 2 nimble,
3 tulips, 4 reflectors, 6 reliable,
7 kindness, 8 spenders,
13 abandoning, 15 scissors,
16 intruded, 17 turn tail,
19 carbon, 20 cirrus, 21 intend.
The challenging race that
appeared in the shaded squares
is "cyclo-cross".

11. Mini Sudoku: Warm-Up

M	P	U	R	W	A
A	R	W	M	U	P
R	M	P	U	A	W
W	U	A	P	R	M
U	W	M	A	P	R
P	A	R	W	M	U

12. Strange But True

b) The groom, Mr U. D. Palmer,
worked at the Borough Cycle
Works and the "cycle wedding"
was the first to be held in
the district.

13. Word Ladder

One possible solution: bike, bake,
rake, race, rack

14. Letter Drop

It is the unknown around the
corner that turns my wheels.

15. Star Name

Chris Froome

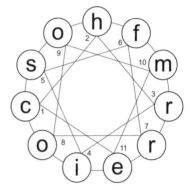

16. Word Quest: Bicycle

Bel, bey, bye, ice, icy, lei, ley, lib,
lie, lye, bice, bile, ceil, lice, cycle,
beylic, bicycle

17. Coded Crossword

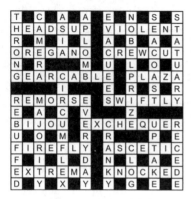

The something challenging for mountain bikers is "rock garden", which is bumpy and challenging terrain.

18. Fitting Words

The words need to be inserted in the following order from top to bottom: toolbox, prizes, chase, fanfare, outfit, rapid, classic. The word created in the shaded squares is "traffic".

19. Bike Jumble

Frame, handlebars, tyres, saddle, reflector, mudguard, breaks, pedals

20. Mystery Sudoku

21. What They Said

1b, 2c, 3a

22. Word Builder

Inner tube

23. Find the Bike

```
E L I B I C B I I C B I C B E
B C L C E Y L Y E L I E L Y E
Y E C Y B E C B C C I C I C C
E B I C I C Y L Y B B E L L B
I B L Y C E C I C L E I C L C
C B E L Y I L C Y B C L Y B E
L I E B L B B C I B L E B Y I
B Y L E I E I L Y C B L L C E
Y B C E L C I C C L B I Y B C
C B I E I B E E L E C L C I E
Y C I C L C I Y I C E B C Y I
B E L L Y B Y E C B Y I L C B
C I B B Y C C B Y L I C Y L E
I L C I E Y L C I C E L C I C
B E B C L I C E L C B I C L B
```

24. A Perplexing Poser

Monday – dynamo

25. Maze

26. Missing Part
Cable

27. Criss-Cross: BMX Tricks

28. Prized Surprise
1 pyjamas, 2 feedback,
3 ballroom, 4 pedals, 5 heroes,
6 showy. In two of the down
columns are the words "yellow jersey" which is much coveted by cyclists in the Tour de France.

29. Strange But True
b) The race was called off following a "stalemate" between police and organizers over plans for the event. A police inspector declared, "It is unacceptable to have masses of cyclists at the side of the road urinating." The story was widely covered by the press and BBC.

30. Cryptogram
The world lies right beyond the handlebars of any bicycle.

31. A Picture Poser
Maintenance (mane, ten ants)

32. Double Take
1 fork, 2 chain, 3 bearing,
4 saddle, 5 nut, 6 gear

33. Mini Sudoku: Sprint

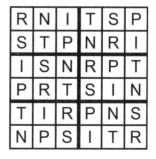

R	N	I	T	S	P
S	T	P	N	R	I
I	S	N	R	P	T
P	R	T	S	I	N
T	I	R	P	N	S
N	P	S	I	T	R

34. Take Your Pick
1c ("bicycle built for two" was a refrain from the song "Daisy Bell" composed by Harry Dacre in 1892), 2a, 3c

35. Star Name
Chris Hoy

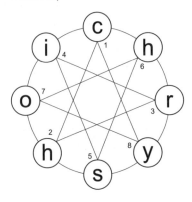

36. Word Search:
Tour de France Winners

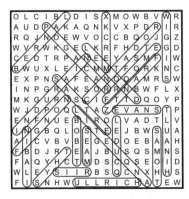

37. Cycling Words
1a, 2c, 3a, 4b

38. Letter Drop
Riding a bike is the closest you can get to flying.

39. Word Ladder
One possible solution: tail, tall, wall, will, wild, wind

40. On Track
Tyre pressure

41. Down Word
Theory, hermit, allows, impact, dental, stylus. The something important for cyclists is "helmet".

42. What Happened Next?
1. The squirrel did not survive the unfortunate encounter.

43. Mystery Sudoku

R	L	C	A	B	N	T	I	U
T	A	I	U	C	R	N	L	B
B	N	U	I	L	T	R	A	C
L	U	B	R	I	C	A	N	T
I	R	T	B	N	A	U	C	L
A	C	N	L	T	U	B	R	I
U	T	A	C	R	I	L	B	N
C	B	R	N	U	L	I	T	A
N	I	L	T	A	B	C	U	R

44. A Riddle
Spoke

45. Coded Crossword

The exciting feature is "chase".

46. Anagram Challenge
1 Tour de France, 2 Giro d'Italia, 3 Vuelta a España. Collectively these three events are known as the "Grand Tours" (roads grunt).

47. National Champions
1e, 2g, 3h, 4i, 5b, 6a, 7j, 8c, 9d, 10f

48. Cross Out
Oil

49. Criss-Cross: Giro d'Italia Winners

50. Strange But True
c) As Koblet had such style and cared about his appearance, he was nicknamed *Le Pédaleur de Charme*.

51. Between the Wheels
Add, hot, owe, ant, why, lid, elk, sly. The discipline hidden between the wheels is "downhill".

52. Cryptogram
Life is like riding a bicycle. To keep your balance you must keep moving. Albert Einstein

53. Word Ladder
One possible solution: bike, like, lice, lick, lock

54. A Perplexing Poser

All the cyclists were married.

55. Acrostics

1 aspect, 2 caught, 3 offset, 4 defect, 5 strike, 6 bypass. The something important and necessary that appears in the shaded squares is "safety checks".

56. Word Search: Winners of the Vuelta a España

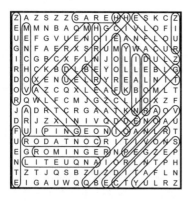

57. What They Said

1a, 2b, 3a

58. Mini Sudoku: Brakes

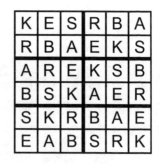

59. Word Builder

Cycle lane

60. A Picture Poser

Mountain biking (mount ten buy king)

61. Anagrams

1 Geraint Thomas, 2 Mark Cavendish, 3 Chris Froome, 4 Jason Kenny, 5 Bradley Wiggins

62. True or False?

1 true, 2 true, 3 false (Eddy Merckx knew from the early age of four that he wanted to be a cyclist), 4 false, 5 true, 6 false (Greg LeMond's first ambition was to become a professional skier)

63. Criss-Cross: Bike Parts

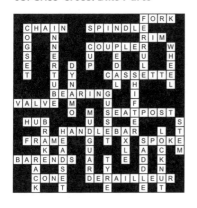

64. Letter Drop

Nothing compares to the simple pleasure of a bike ride.

65. Take Your Pick

1b, 2c, 3c

66. Cycling Words

1a, 2b, 3b, 4c

67. How Many?

13. This includes the "c" in "How many letter C's are there on this page?" If you included this one, well done for "c ing"!

68. Star Name

Mark Cavendish

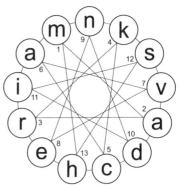

69. Spot the Difference

See the solution at the end of this section.

70. Coded Crossword

The race is "keirin" in which cyclists follow a motorized vehicle, usually a motorcycle, for so many laps before sprinting to the finish. Developed in Japan, it is now an Olympic event.

71. Maze

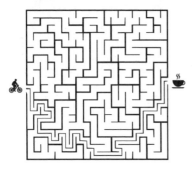

72. Word Search

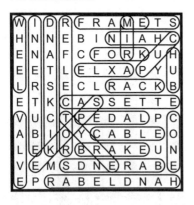

The something useful was "bicycle pump".

73. What They Said

1a, 2c, 3c

74. Mystery Sudoku

75. A Perplexing Poser

The cyclist was on foot.

76. Double Take

1 suspension, 2 grip, 3 stem, 4 crank, 5 frame, 6 light

77. Word Ladder

One possible solution: ring, wing, wind, wild, will, well, bell

78. Mystery Word Search

The hazards and mishaps are pothole, crash, fall, skid, puncture and collide, and they are hidden as shown.

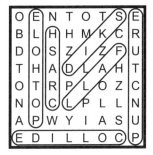

79. Criss-Cross: Bike Makes

80. Word Builder
Breakaway

81. A Picture Poser
Cartridge bearing (cart ridge bear ring)

82. Cryptogram
Think of bicycles as rideable art that can just about save the world.

83. Strange But True
b)

84. Word Search: Olympic and Paralympic Medallists

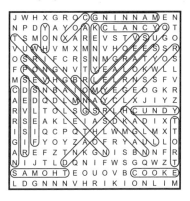

85. Word Link
1 soft, 2 turn, 3 stay, 4 time, 5 open. The word in the shaded column is "frame".

86. Mini Sudoku: Presta

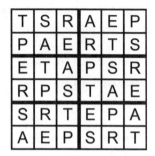

T	S	R	A	E	P
P	A	E	R	T	S
E	T	A	P	S	R
R	P	S	T	A	E
S	R	T	E	P	A
A	E	P	S	R	T

87. Fitting Words

The words need to be inserted in the following order from top to bottom: mitts, gusset, pedal, gears, ferrule, brake, shifter, hybrid. The word created in the shaded squares is "mudguard".

88. Spot the Difference

See the solution at the end of this section.

89. Anagrams

1 tandem, 2 road bike,
3 mountain bike, 4 recumbent,
5 penny-farthing

90. A Picture Poser

Four-cross, a style of mountain bike racing

91. Letter Drop

I'm the reference point. If they beat me, they win.

92. Maze

93. Word Ladder

One possible solution: fast, cast, case, came, tame, time

94. What They Said

1a, 2b, 3c

95. Coded Crossword

Eddy Merckx's advice was "Ride lots".

96. Star Name
Laura Kenny

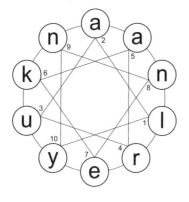

97. Down the Middle
Road race

98. Cross Out
Tyre

99. A Picture Poser
Drop handlebar brakes (drop hand doll bar breaks)

100. Mystery Sudoku

T	L	R	U	Y	O	N	E	C
N	Y	E	R	T	C	O	U	L
O	U	C	E	N	L	T	R	Y
Y	R	U	O	C	E	L	T	N
E	N	T	Y	L	U	C	O	R
L	C	O	N	R	T	E	Y	U
U	T	L	C	O	Y	R	N	E
R	O	Y	L	E	N	U	C	T
C	E	N	T	U	R	Y	L	O

Given that this puzzle is the hundredth in the book, the apt word was "century" and in cycling this means a 100-mile ride or race. A 100-kilometre ride or race is called a "metric century" which is just over 62 miles.

101. Cycling Words
1c, 2a, 3b, 4a

102. Cryptogram
I relax by taking my bicycle apart and putting it back together again.

103. Word Search

Iain MacGregor considered the Paris–Roubaix to be "the toughest race in cycling".

104. A Perplexing Poser
Three

105. What They Said
1c, 2c, 3a

106. Word Ladder
One possible solution: flat, feat, beat, bent, bend, band, land

107. Anagrams
1 front wheel, 2 brakes, 3 suspension fork, 4 reflectors, 5 chainstay

108. Mini Sudoku: Hybrid

B	R	D	H	I	Y
Y	I	H	D	R	B
D	B	Y	R	H	I
I	H	R	Y	B	D
H	D	I	B	Y	R
R	Y	B	I	D	H

109. Who?
1 Eddy Merckx, 2 Chris Hoy, 3 John Lennon, 4 Freddie Mercury, 5 Geraint Thomas, 6 Mark Twain

110. Criss-Cross: Vuelta a España Winners

111. Strange But True
c)

112. Spot the Difference
See the solution at the end of this section.

113. Acrostics
1 follow, 2 radish, 3 orange, 4 needle, 5 travel. The words in the shaded squares are "front wheel".

114. Mystery Sudoku

S	P	N	E	B	R	H	I	A
I	R	H	A	S	N	P	E	B
E	B	A	P	I	H	S	R	N
A	S	E	B	H	P	R	N	I
R	H	I	N	E	A	B	S	P
P	N	B	I	R	S	E	A	H
B	A	R	S	P	I	N	H	E
N	E	S	H	A	B	I	P	R
H	I	P	R	N	E	A	B	S

Barspin is a popular and impressive BMX trick.

115. Cross Out
Grips

116. Nicknames
1d, 2f, 3a, 4i, 5b, 6j, 7e, 8c, 9g, 10h

117. Word Link
1 best, 2 pipe, 3 show, 4 take, 5 deep. The word in the shaded column is "spoke".

118. Anagrams
1 bunnyhop, 2 superman, 3 nothing, 4 candy bar, 5 seat grab

119. Word Search: Bike Parts

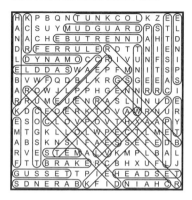

120. Letter Drop
A bicycle ride around the world begins with a single pedal stroke.

121. Cycling Words
1c, 2c, 3b, 4a

122. Mini Sudoku: Tandem

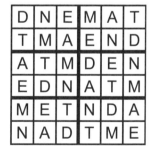

D	N	E	M	A	T
T	M	A	E	N	D
A	T	M	D	E	N
E	D	N	A	T	M
M	E	T	N	D	A
N	A	D	T	M	E

123. Coded Crossword

What cyclists (and others) like to achieve is their "personal best".

124. Maze

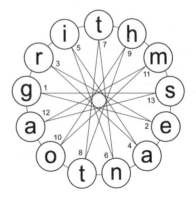

125. Word Builder
Handlebar

126. Cryptogram
What's the difference between a well-dressed cyclist and a scruffy one on a tricycle? A tyre (attire).

127. Take Your Pick
1c (Paul is an "extreme ironing" enthusiast and, in addition to his cycling achievements, completed the 155-mile-long desert marathon, the Marathon des Sables, with an ironing board on his back), 2a, 3b

128. A Perplexing Poser
Second. As Sara overtook the cyclist in second position, she became the second cyclist, and was still behind the cyclist in first place. A valiant effort nevertheless.

129. Cross Out
Ramps

130. Star Name
Geraint Thomas

131. Strange But True
a)

132. Word Ladder
One possible solution: milk, mile, mice, rice, race

133. Mystery Sudoku

134. Criss-Cross:
Winners of the Grand Tours

135. Acrostics
1 sleuth, 2 admire, 3 Delphi, 4 daring, 5 length, 6 escort. The words in the shaded squares spell "saddle height".

136. What They Said
1c, 2b, 3a

137. Mystery Word Search

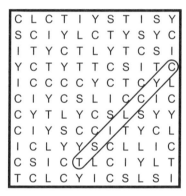

138. Surprise Prize
1c, 2f, 3a, 4b, 5d, 6e

139. On Track
Electric bike

140. Take Your Pick
1a, 2c, 3c

141. Mini Sudoku: Grinds

R	G	I	D	S	N
N	S	D	R	G	I
G	N	R	I	D	S
D	I	S	N	R	G
S	R	N	G	I	D
I	D	G	S	N	R

142. Strange But True

b)

143. Letter Drop

The bicycle is a curious vehicle. Its passenger is its engine.

144. X

When the words are entered in the following order – skater, italic, hurdle, friend, answer, gadget – the BMX discipline of "street riding" appears in the shaded squares.

145. Spot the Difference

See the solution at the end of this section.

146. Word Builder

Grand Tour

147. Crossword

Across: 1 patron, 4 brooch, 8 deflate, 9 already, 11 Eddy Merckx, 12 alas, 13 droop, 14 euphoric, 16 dramatic, 18 chain, 20 ajar, 21 Greg LeMond, 23 empiric, 24 stadium, 25 stress, 26 crisis.

Down: 1 plead, 2 tally-ho, 3 on-the-spot, 5 relax, 6 oregano, 7 hydration, 10 screeched, 13 dirt jumps, 15 peculator, 17 merrier, 19 armadas, 21 grips, 22 nouns.

It was "a horse" which joined and led the 1997 Critérium International race in France. It could well have won but decided to stop for a graze 19 km from the finish.

148. Word Ladder

One possible solution: hold, bold, bond, band, bank, back

149. Cross Out

Vert is a discipline in Freestyle BMX.

150. Anagrams

1 disc brake, 2 derailleur, 3 wingnut, 4 spindle, 5 dynamo

151. Mystery Sudoku

M	A	D	I	S	O	N	E	L
I	N	E	M	L	D	O	S	A
S	L	O	E	N	A	I	M	D
D	I	A	S	M	N	E	L	O
E	M	L	D	O	I	S	A	N
N	O	S	L	A	E	M	D	I
L	S	N	O	D	M	A	I	E
O	E	M	A	I	L	D	N	S
A	D	I	N	E	S	L	O	M

The Madison is a relay race event in track cycling; it's raced by teams of two.

152. Trail Finder

1i, 2f, 3h, 4b, 5a, 6c, 7e, 8d, 9g

153. Word Link

1 high, 2 over, 3 head, 4 work, 5 case. The word in the shaded column is "gears".

154. Criss-Cross: Race Across America

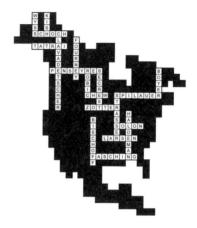

155. A Picture Poser

Bunny hop (bun knee hop)

156. Hidden Parts

1 fork, 2 wheel, 3 tyre, 4 spoke, 5 stem

157. On the Right Track

Charity bike rides

158. Letter Drop

When it's hurting you, that's when you can make a difference.

159. Acrostics

1 sharp, 2 karma, 3 after, 4 think, 5 exits. The words in the shaded squares are "skate parks".

160. Strange But True

c)

161. Word Search: BMX Tricks

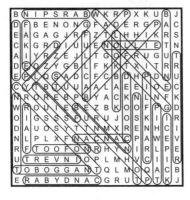

162. Maze

163. Missing Part

Lever

164. What They Said

1c, 2c, 3b

165. Word Ladder

One possible solution: slow, slot, soot, soon, sown, down

166. Criss-Cross: Santos Tour Down Under

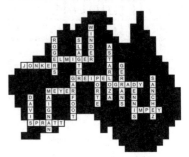

167. Fitting Words

When the words are entered in the following order – superb, stupor, guitar, outcry, clocks, employ – the words "sticky bottle" appear in the shaded squares. This is the practice where a cyclist is handed a water bottle by an occupant in a car and both hold on to the bottle, resulting in the bike being helped along by the car.

168. Bike Parts Medley

1 frame, wheel, 2 cable, pedal, 3 spoke, valve, 4 chain, brake

169. Anagram Challenge

"Irk pirate" is an anagram of "repair kit" and the other anagrams are items often found in a kit. 1 tyre patch, 2 tyre levers, 3 adhesive, 4 sandpaper

170. Mystery Sudoku

E	L	H	P	N	S	I	O	D
N	O	P	D	L	I	H	E	S
I	D	S	O	E	H	N	L	P
P	I	E	L	S	D	O	N	H
D	N	O	H	P	E	L	S	I
H	S	L	I	O	N	D	P	E
O	H	N	E	I	P	S	D	L
L	E	D	S	H	O	P	I	N
S	P	I	N	D	L	E	H	O

171. A Perplexing Poser

The cyclist stood the signpost up so that the arm pointing to and naming the village she had just cycled from was pointed in the correct direction. With one arm pointing the right way, the other arms would also be correct.

172. Letter Drop

I like to go fast, and use my brakes as little as possible.

173. Spot the Difference

See the solution at the end of this section.

174. Word Builder

Time trial

175. Cryptogram

Whoever invented the bicycle deserves the thanks of humanity.

176. Mini Sudoku: Trails

R	T	I	L	A	S
L	S	A	I	R	T
I	R	S	T	L	A
A	L	T	S	I	R
T	I	R	A	S	L
S	A	L	R	T	I

177. Word Ladder

One possible solution: nose, none, nine, nice, nick, pick

178. A Picture Poser

Saddle sores (sad doll saws). This was why there was a hint of apology.

179. Acrostics

1 bottle, 2 regret, 3 active, 4 kennel, 5 encore. The important bike part in the shaded squares is "brake lever".

180. Find the Puncture

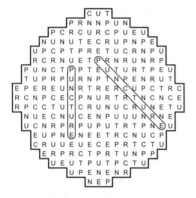

181. Take Your Pick

1a, 2a (the yellow jersey had been made from a mix of synthetic yarn and wool and Bobet said it would make him sweat too much), 3b (because Binda was such a dominant force and made the outcome of the race inevitable (and less exciting), the organizers paid him the equivalent of the prize money to stay away)

182. A Perplexing Poser

The letter "e"

183. Cycling Words

1c, 2a, 3b, 4b

184. Word Link

1 back, 2 dead, 3 baby, 4 pull, 5 keep. The word in the shaded column is "cable".

185. Crossword

Across: 1 pacers, 4 Badger, 9 fork, 10 journalist, 11 missed, 12 landmark, 13 road metal, 15 edge, 16 dash, 17 pedalling, 21 double up, 22 valves, 24 sweatbands, 25 calm, 26 yields, 27 drills.
Down: 1 proviso, 2 cakes, 3 rejudge, 5 awning, 6 gold medal, 7 reserve, 8 Vuelta a España, 14 disc brake, 16 doorway, 18 adviser, 19 needles, 20 seabed, 23 local. The word in the shaded squares is "criterium" – this is a race consisting of a specified number of laps on a closed circuit.

186. Anagrams

1 bearings, 2 gears, 3 sprockets, 4 chainset, 5 cassette

187. Letter Drop
You are one ride away from a good mood.

188. Mini Sudoku: Lights

G	H	T	S	I	L
S	I	L	H	G	T
I	G	H	T	L	S
L	T	S	I	H	G
H	S	G	L	T	I
T	L	I	G	S	H

189. Missing Part
Valve

190. What They Said
1c, 2c, 3a

191. A Perplexing Poser
Charlie, Jess, Eduardo, Terri, Maria

192. Cryptogram
After a long day on my bicycle, I feel refreshed, cleansed, purified.

193. Word Builder
Reflector

194. Cross Out
Spin

195. Mystery Sudoku

R	E	B	L	A	I	D	S	N
S	I	A	D	B	N	E	R	L
L	N	D	R	E	S	A	I	B
B	A	R	E	N	D	S	L	I
N	L	S	A	I	B	R	D	E
E	D	I	S	L	R	N	B	A
I	S	N	B	D	A	L	E	R
A	R	L	I	S	E	B	N	D
D	B	E	N	R	L	I	A	S

196. Anagrams
1 spanner, 2 pliers, 3 Allen key, 4 bicycle pump, 5 socket wrench

197. Fitting Words
The words need to be entered in the following order: scruff, sprain, corner, skiing, ascend, helmet. The words in the shaded squares are "sprint finish".

198. Criss-Cross: The Greats

199. Strange But True

b)

200. Between the Wheels

Act, she, fan, emu, spa, lip, row, end. The word between the wheels, and which is true of many named in the book and of you for succeeding in so many puzzles, is "champion".

SPOT THE DIFFERENCE
ANSWERS

9. Spot the Difference

69. Spot the Difference

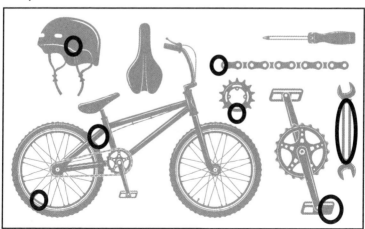

88. Spot the Difference

112. Spot the Difference

145. Spot the Difference

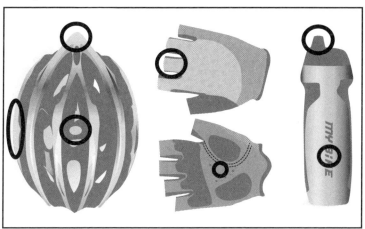

173. Spot the Difference

ACKNOWLEDGEMENTS

Fresh air. Freedom.
My bike and I in harmony.

Cycling means so much to so many and during the compilation of this book I have been really grateful for the interest and help that others have so willingly given. My family – Ros, Richard and Emily – have, as always, been willing to try out puzzles and give valuable input.

I would also like to thank David Finnerty for his technical expertise and readiness to offer advice, and thanks too to Marion and David Parkinson and David Isaacs for their help. This was much appreciated.

As always it was a joy to work with such a dedicated team at Summersdale, and especial thanks go to Robert Drew, my editor, and Claire Plimmer. Their guidance made a difference. Many thanks as well to Derek Donnelly, whose proofreading was invaluable. Last but not least, I would like to thank you, the reader, for your interest and support. It is you that makes this so worthwhile.

ABOUT THE AUTHOR

Neil Somerville is a keen cyclist and especially enjoys cycling across country (the bumpier the better!) and exploring cycle trails. His rides have taken him to lots of places, bringing him and his family many happy and memorable times.

When not out and about, Neil writes and sets puzzles. He has written and compiled many bestselling books, including *For the Love of Radio 4: The Unofficial Puzzle Book*, *For the Love of The Archers: The Unofficial Puzzle Book*, *The Literary Pocket Puzzle Book*, *Cat Wisdom: 60 Great Lessons You Can Learn from a Cat* and a long-running series on Chinese horoscopes. He also contributes to newspapers and magazines and has compiled puzzles for *The Countryman* for many years.

Neil lives in Berkshire with his wife. He has two adult children and a shed containing quite a few bikes. His website is **www.neilsomerville.com**.

If you're interested in finding out more about our books,
find us on Facebook at **Summersdale Publishers**,
on Twitter at **@Summersdale** and on Instagram at
@summersdalebooks and get in touch.
We'd love to hear from you!

www.summersdale.com

Image credits